GRADE 4

Curriculum Units

1 | **Factors, Multiples, and Arrays**
Multiplication and Division 1

2 | **Describing the Shape of the Data**
Data Analysis and Probability

3 | **Multiple Towers and Division Stories**
Multiplication and Division 2

4 | **Size, Shape, and Symmetry**
2-D Geometry and Measurement

5 | **Landmarks and Large Numbers**
Addition, Subtraction, and the Number System

6 | **Fraction Cards and Decimal Squares**
Fractions and Decimals

7 | **Moving Between Solids and Silhouettes**
3-D Geometry and Measurement

8 | **How Many Packages? How Many Groups?**
Multiplication and Division 3

9 | **Penny Jars and Plant Growth**
Patterns, Functions, and Change

Fraction Cards and Decimal Squares

Fractions and Decimals

UNIT 6

Polished Spiral Karin Kuhlmann

"Although the creation of fractals is bounded to strict mathematical rules, the results are always very inspiring."– **Karin Kuhlmann**

Investigations
IN NUMBER, DATA, AND SPACE®

PEARSON
Scott
Foresman
scottforesman.com

Editorial offices: Glenview, Illinois • Parsippany, New Jersey • New York, New York
Sales offices: Boston, Massachusetts • Duluth, Georgia
Glenview, Illinois • Coppell, Texas • Sacramento, California • Mesa, Arizona

T E R C

The Investigations curriculum was developed by TERC, Cambridge, MA.

NSF

This material is based on work supported by the National Science Foundation ("NSF") under Grant No. ESI-0095450. Any opinions, findings, and conclusions or recommendations expressed in this material are those of the author(s) and do not necessarily reflect the views of the National Science Foundation.

ISBN: 0-328-23758-2

ISBN: 978-0-328-23758-6

7 8 9 10-V003-15 14 13 12 11 10 09 08
CC:N3

T E R C

Co-Principal Investigators

Susan Jo Russell

Karen Economopoulos

Authors

Lucy Wittenberg
Director Grades 3–5

Karen Economopoulos
Director Grades K–2

Virginia Bastable
(SummerMath for Teachers,
Mt. Holyoke College)

Katie Hickey Bloomfield

Keith Cochran

Darrell Earnest

Arusha Hollister

Nancy Horowitz

Erin Leidl

Megan Murray

Young Oh

Beth W. Perry

Susan Jo Russell

Deborah Schifter
(Education
Development Center)

Kathy Sillman

Administrative Staff

Amy Taber
Project Manager

Beth Bergeron

Lorraine Brooks

Emi Fujiwara

Contributing Authors

Denise Baumann

Jennifer DiBrienza

Hollee Freeman

Paula Hooper

Jan Mokros

Stephen Monk
(University of Washington)

Mary Beth O'Connor

Judy Storeygard

Cornelia Tierney

Elizabeth Van Cleef

Carol Wright

Technology

Jim Hammerman

Classroom Field Work

Amy Appell

Rachel E. Davis

Traci Higgins

Julia Thompson

Collaborating Teachers

This group of dedicated teachers carried out extensive field testing in their classrooms, met regularly to discuss issues of teaching and learning mathematics, provided feedback to staff, welcomed staff into their classrooms to document students' work, and contributed both suggestions and written material that has been incorporated into the curriculum.

Bethany Altchek

Linda Amaral

Kimberly Beauregard

Barbara Bernard

Nancy Buell

Rose Christiansen

Chris Colbath-Hess

Lisette Colon

Kim Cook

Frances Cooper

Kathleen Drew

Rebeka Eston Salemi

Thomas Fisher

Michael Flynn

Holly Ghazey

Susan Gillis

Danielle Harrington

Elaine Herzog

Francine Hiller

Kirsten Lee Howard

Liliana Klass

Leslie Kramer

Melissa Lee Andrichak

Kelley Lee Sadowski

Jennifer Levitan

Mary Lou LoVecchio

Kristen McEnaney

Maura McGrail

Kathe Millett

Florence Molyneaux

Amy Monkiewicz

Elizabeth Monopoli

Carol Murray

Robyn Musser

Christine Norrman

Deborah O'Brien

Timothy O'Connor

Anne Marie O'Reilly

Mark Paige

Margaret Riddle

Karen Schweitzer

Elisabeth Seyferth

Susan Smith

Debra Sorvillo

Shoshanah Starr

Janice Szymaszek

Karen Tobin

JoAnn Trauschke

Ana Vaisenstein

Yvonne Watson

Michelle Woods

Mary Wright

Note: Unless otherwise noted, all contributors listed above were staff of the Education Research Collaborative at TERC during their work on the curriculum. Other affiliations during the time of development are listed.

Advisors

Deborah Lowenberg Ball,
University of Michigan

Hyman Bass, Professor of Mathematics and Mathematics Education
University of Michigan

Mary Canner, Principal, Natick Public Schools

Thomas Carpenter, Professor of Curriculum and Instruction,
University of Wisconsin-Madison

Janis Freckmann, Elementary Mathematics Coordinator,
Milwaukee Public Schools

Lynne Godfrey, Mathematics Coach,
Cambridge Public Schools

Ginger Hanlon, Instructional Specialist in Mathematics,
New York City Public Schools

DeAnn Huinker, Director, Center for Mathematics and
Science Education Research, University of Wisconsin-Milwaukee

James Kaput, Professor of Mathematics, University of
Massachusetts-Dartmouth

Kate Kline, Associate Professor, Department of Mathematics
and Statistics, Western Michigan University

Jim Lewis, Professor of Mathematics,
University of Nebraska-Lincoln

William McCallum, Professor of Mathematics,
University of Arizona

Harriet Pollatsek, Professor of Mathematics,
Mount Holyoke College

Debra Shein-Gerson, Elementary Mathematics Specialist,
Weston Public Schools

Gary Shevell, Assistant Principal,
New York City Public Schools

Liz Sweeney, Elementary Math Department,
Boston Public Schools

Lucy West, Consultant, Metamorphosis:
Teaching Learning Communities, Inc.

This revision of the curriculum was built on the work of the many authors who contributed to the first edition (published between 1994 and 1998). We acknowledge the critical contributions of these authors in developing the content and pedagogy of *Investigations*:

Authors

Joan Akers

Michael T. Battista

Douglas H. Clements

Karen Economopoulos

Marlene Kliman

Jan Mokros

Megan Murray

Ricardo Nemirovsky

Andee Rubin

Susan Jo Russell

Cornelia Tierney

Contributing Authors

Mary Berle-Carman

Rebecca B. Corwin

Rebeka Eston

Claryce Evans

Anne Goodrow

Cliff Konold

Chris Mainhart

Sue McMillen

Jerrie Moffet

Tracy Noble

Kim O'Neil

Mark Ogonowski

Julie Sarama

Amy Shulman Weinberg

Margie Singer

Virginia Woolley

Tracey Wright

Contents

UNIT 6

Fraction Cards and Decimal Squares

INTRODUCTION AND OVERVIEW

Investigations Curriculum	6
Overview of This Unit	8
Mathematics in This Unit	10
Assessment in This Unit	14
Ten-Minute Math in This Unit	16
Practice and Review in This Unit	17
Differentiation in This Unit	18

INVESTIGATION 1

Parts of Rectangles

INVESTIGATION 1 PLANNER	20
SESSION 1.1 Fractions of an Area: Halves, Fourths, and Eighths	24
SESSION 1.2 Fractions of an Area: Thirds and Sixths	32
SESSION 1.3 Fractions of Groups of Things	37
SESSION 1.4 Same Parts, Different Wholes	41
SESSION 1.5 Assessment: Identifying and Comparing Fractions	47
SESSION 1.6 Combinations That Equal 1	52
SESSION 1.7 Adding Fractions	58

-1.8 A Sub.fractions

INVESTIGATION 2

Ordering Fractions

INVESTIGATION 2 PLANNER	64
SESSION 2.1 Fraction Cards	68
SESSION 2.2 Fraction Cards, *continued*	74
SESSION 2.3 Capture Fractions	78
SESSION 2.4 Comparing Fractions to Landmarks	83
SESSION 2.5 Fractions on a Number Line	88
SESSION 2.6 Assessment: Comparing Fractions	94

CMT-   2.7A Add/Sub Mixed Number

INVESTIGATION 3

Working With Decimals

INVESTIGATION 3 PLANNER	100
SESSION 3.1 Representing Decimals	104
SESSION 3.2 Comparing Decimals	111
SESSION 3.3 Representing and Combining Decimals	116
SESSION 3.4 Estimating and Adding Miles and Tenths of a Mile	120
SESSION 3.5 Comparing and Combining Decimals	127
SESSION 3.6 Comparing and Combining Decimals, *continued*	132
SESSION 3.7 End-of-Unit Assessment	135

Teacher Notes	139
Dialogue Boxes	164
Student Math Handbook	170
Index	177

Investigations

Overview of Program Components

FOR TEACHERS

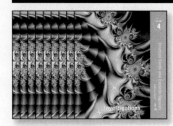

The **Curriculum Units** are the teaching guides. (See far right.)

Implementing Investigations in Grade 4 offers suggestions for implementing the curriculum. It also contains a comprehensive index.

The **Resources Binder** contains all the Resource Masters and Transparencies that support instruction. (Also available on CD) The binder also includes a student software CD.

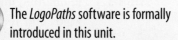

The *LogoPaths* software is formally introduced in this unit.

FOR STUDENTS

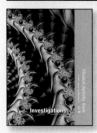

The **Student Activity Book** contains the consumable student pages (Recording Sheets, Homework, Practice, and so on).

The **Student Math Handbook** contains Math Words and Ideas pages and Games directions.

The *Investigations* Curriculum

Investigations in Number, Data, and Space® is a K–5 mathematics curriculum designed to engage students in making sense of mathematical ideas. Six major goals guided the development of the *Investigations in Number, Data, and Space®* curriculum. The curriculum is designed to:

- Support students to make sense of mathematics and learn that they can be mathematical thinkers

- Focus on computational fluency with whole numbers as a major goal of the elementary grades

- Provide substantive work in important areas of mathematics—rational numbers, geometry, measurement, data, and early algebra—and connections among them

- Emphasize reasoning about mathematical ideas

- Communicate mathematics content and pedagogy to teachers

- Engage the range of learners in understanding mathematics

Underlying these goals are three guiding principles that are touchstones for the *Investigations* team as we approach both students and teachers as agents of their own learning:

1. *Students have mathematical ideas.* Students come to school with ideas about numbers, shapes, measurements, patterns, and data. If given the opportunity to learn in an environment that stresses making sense of mathematics, students build on the ideas they already have and learn about new mathematics they have never encountered. Students learn that they are capable of having mathematical ideas, applying what they know to new situations, and thinking and reasoning about unfamiliar problems.

2. *Teachers are engaged in ongoing learning* about mathematics content, pedagogy, and student learning. The curriculum provides material for professional development, to be used by teachers individually or in groups, that supports teachers' continued learning as they use the curriculum over several years. The *Investigations* curriculum materials are designed as much to be a dialogue with teachers as to be a core of content for students.

3. *Teachers collaborate with the students and curriculum materials* to create the curriculum as enacted in the classroom. The only way for a good curriculum to be used well is for teachers to be active participants in implementing it. Teachers use the curriculum to maintain a clear, focused, and coherent agenda for mathematics teaching. At the same time, they observe and listen carefully to students, try to understand how they are thinking, and make teaching decisions based on these observations.

Investigations is based on experience from research and practice, including field testing that involved documentation of thousands of hours in classrooms, observations of students, input from teachers, and analysis of student work. As a result, the curriculum addresses the learning needs of real students in a wide range of classrooms and communities. The investigations are carefully designed to invite all students into mathematics—girls and boys; members of diverse cultural, ethnic, and language groups; and students with a wide variety of strengths, needs, and interests.

Based on this extensive classroom testing, the curriculum takes seriously the time students need to develop a strong conceptual foundation and skills based on that foundation. Each curriculum unit focuses on an area of content in depth, providing time for students to develop and practice ideas across a variety of activities and contexts that build on each other. Daily guidelines for time spent on class sessions, Classroom Routines (K–3), and Ten-Minute Math (3–5) reflect the commitment to devoting adequate time to mathematics in each school day.

About This Curriculum Unit

This **Curriculum Unit** is one of nine teaching guides in Grade 4. The sixth unit in Grade 4 is *Fraction Cards and Decimal Squares.*

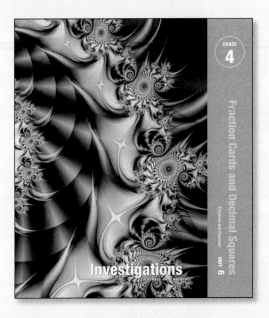

- The **Introduction and Overview** section organizes and presents the instructional materials, provides background information, and highlights important features specific to this unit.

- Each Curriculum Unit contains several **Investigations.** Each Investigation focuses on a set of related mathematical ideas.

- Investigations are divided into one-hour **Sessions,** or lessons.

- Sessions have a combination of these parts: **Activity, Discussion, Math Workshop, Assessment Activity,** and **Session Follow-Up.**

- Each session also has one or more **Ten-Minute Math** activities that are done outside of math time.

- At the back of the book is a collection of **Teacher Notes** and **Dialogue Boxes** that provide professional development related to the unit.

- Also included at the back of the book are the **Student Math Handbook** pages for this unit.

- The **Index** provides a way to look up important words or terms.

Overview

O F   T H I S   U N I T

Investigation	Session	Day	
INVESTIGATION 1 ## Parts of Rectangles Students find fractional parts of the area of different-sized rectangles and of groups of objects or people. They compare fractions and find combinations of fractions that are equal to 1. Using representations and mathematical reasoning, students add fractions with like and unlike denominators. *Stress equal parts*	**1.1** Fractions of an Area: Halves, Fourths, and Eighths	1	
	1.2 Fractions of an Area: Thirds and Sixths	2	
	1.3 Fractions of Groups of Things	3	
	1.4 Same Parts, Different Wholes	4	
	1.5 Assessment: Identifying and Comparing Fractions	5	
	1.6 Combinations That Equal 1	6	
	1.7 Adding Fractions	7	
INVESTIGATION 2 ## Ordering Fractions Students make Fraction Cards that show area representations for fractions and mixed numbers. They compare fractions to the landmarks $0, \frac{1}{2}, 1,$ and 2, and place fractions and mixed numbers on a number line. Students make conjectures about general rules for comparing fractions.	**2.1** Fraction Cards	8	
	2.2 Fraction Cards, *continued*	9	
	2.3 Capture Fractions	10	
	2.4 Comparing Fractions to Landmarks	11	
	2.5 Fractions on a Number Line	12	
	2.6 Assessment: Comparing Fractions	13	
INVESTIGATION 3 ## Working With Decimals Students represent and compare decimals using 10×10 squares. They use representations to combine decimals that include tenths and hundredths. Using a context of running or walking, students add distances in miles and in tenths and hundredths of a mile.	**3.1** Representing Decimals	14	
	3.2 Comparing Decimals	15	
	3.3 Representing and Combining Decimals	16	
	3.4 Estimating and Adding Miles and Tenths of a Mile	17	
	3.5 Comparing and Combining Decimals	18	
	3.6 Comparing and Combining Decimals, *continued*	19	
	3.7 End-of-Unit Assessment	20	

Each *Investigations* session has some combination of these five parts: **Activity, Discussion, Math Workshop, Assessment Activity,** and **Session Follow-Up.** These session parts are indicated in the chart below. Each session also has one or more **Ten-Minute Math** activities that are done outside of math time.

Ten-Minute Math

Activity	Discussion	Math Workshop	Assessment Activity	Session Follow-Up	Practicing Place Value	Quick Survey
●●				●	●	
●	●			●	●	
●●				●	●	
	●	●		●	●	
●			●	●	●	
●		●		●	●	
	●	●		●	●	
●	●			●		●
●	●			●		●
●	●			●		●
●●				●		●
●	●	●		●		●
	●	●	●	●		●
●●	●			●	●	
●●				●	●	
●	●			●	●	
●●	●			●	●	
	●	●		●	●	
		●		●	●	
			●	●	●	

Mathematics

IN THIS UNIT

Fraction Cards and Decimal Squares is the only Grade 4 fractions unit. It builds on the work in the Grade 3 unit, *Finding Fair Shares,* in which students work to understand fractions as equal parts, identify equivalent fractions, and combine fractions with denominators that are the same as well as different.

LOOKING BACK

In Grades 2 and 3, students built an understanding of the meaning of fractions and their relationships. In the context of equal shares, they worked with fractions as parts of a single object ($\frac{1}{3}$ of a brownie), an area ($\frac{1}{3}$ of the surface of a hexagonal pattern block), or a group of things ($\frac{1}{3}$ of the class). Students learned the meanings of the numerator and denominator of a fraction. As they worked with halves, fourths, and eighths, and with thirds and sixths, they gained experience with equivalent fractions, for example, that three sixths and two fourths are both equal to one half of the same whole. Students developed strong visual images of many of these fractions and fraction equivalencies by using pattern blocks and rectangles. They also worked with fractions greater than 1. In Grade 3, students encountered the most familiar decimal fractions, such as 0.5 and 0.25, in the context of money, and became familiar with fraction and decimal equivalents involving halves and fourths.

In this unit, students work with fractions that represent halves, thirds, fourths, fifths, sixths, eighths, tenths, and twelfths, and decimal fractions in tenths and hundredths.

This unit focuses on 3 Mathematical Emphases:

1 Rational Numbers Understanding the meaning of fractions and decimal fractions

Math Focus Points

- Finding fractional parts of a rectangular area
- Finding fractional parts of a group (of objects, people, etc.)

- Interpreting the meaning of the numerator and the denominator of a fraction
- Writing, reading, and applying fraction notation
- Representing fractions greater than 1
- Identifying everyday uses of fractions and decimals
- Reading and writing tenths and hundredths
- Representing tenths and hundredths as parts of an area

Students continue to work with fractions in the context of area (equal parts of a rectangle) and a group of things (e.g., a fractional part of the class). Through the use of the Fraction Cards, students visualize how fractions are related to 1 as equal parts of a whole and how they are related to one another. These representations are important references for students' understanding of fractions, and help students develop mental images of these numbers.

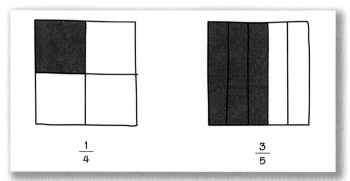

$$\frac{1}{4} \qquad\qquad \frac{3}{5}$$

Fraction Cards

Students continue to focus on the meaning of fractions as equal parts of a whole (thing, area, group). Understanding that fractions refer to equal parts entails both recognizing fractional parts of an area or a group, and being able to divide a whole into fractional parts. It requires an understanding that the denominator of a fraction indicates the number of equal parts into which a whole is divided, and the numerator indicates how many of those parts are being considered.

Students extend their images of equal parts to accommodate fractions that are greater than 1. Students often find the meaning of these fractions, such as $\frac{5}{3}$, more difficult to understand: how can there be five equal pieces if the whole is divided into only three parts? Visualizing fractions that are greater than 1 is an important part of their work in Grade 4. Students learn that these numbers can be written as fractions ($\frac{5}{3}$) or as mixed numbers ($1\frac{2}{3}$).

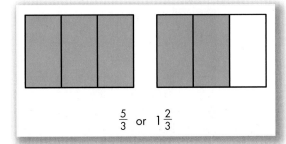

$$\frac{5}{3} \quad \text{or} \quad 1\frac{2}{3}$$

Students also work with the idea that the same fraction can represent different quantities, depending on the size of the whole. One quarter of the floor of a basketball court is a different size from one quarter of the surface of a sandwich. $\frac{2}{3}$ of my set of marbles is not the same as $\frac{2}{3}$ of all the marbles at the store.

Students extend their use of the number line to represent whole numbers to include numbers less than 1. Although in a practical situation, a fraction represents a part of a particular whole ($\frac{1}{2}$ of the marbles, $\frac{1}{2}$ of the rectangle) and can represent a variety of quantities ($\frac{1}{2}$ of 24 marbles is 12 marbles; $\frac{1}{2}$ of 60 square units is 30 square units), a fraction is also a *number* that always has the same relationship to 1 and to other numbers. Using the number line emphasizes that a fraction is a number. Just as 150 has a certain position on the number line in relation to other numbers, so does a fraction such as $\frac{1}{2}$. As students use and reflect on a variety of representations for fractions, such as rectangles, groups of things, and the number line, they deepen their understanding of the meaning of fractions.

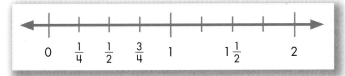

Students are introduced to tenths and hundredths as an extension of the place-value system they have studied for whole numbers. As they represent 0.1 and 0.01 as parts of a rectangle, they see that one tenth is equivalent to ten hundredths and that ten tenths is equivalent to 1. They also relate decimals to familiar fractions and to other decimals; for example, when they represent 0.25, they can see how it is equal to $\frac{1}{4}$ and to $2\frac{1}{2}$ tenths. You might think of students' experience with decimals in Grade 4 as parallel to their experience with fractions in Grade 3. They need time and focus to develop a sound understanding of what these numbers mean (see the **Teacher Note:** Extending Place Value to Tenths and Hundredths, page 157), how they are related to whole numbers, and how they are related to fractions.

2 Rational Numbers Comparing the values of fractions and decimal fractions

Math Focus Points

◆ Identifying relationships between unit fractions when one denominator is a multiple of the other (e.g., halves and fourths, thirds and sixths)

◆ Comparing the same fractional parts of different-sized wholes

◆ Identifying equivalent fractions

◆ Ordering fractions and justifying their order through reasoning about fraction equivalencies and relationships

◆ Representing fractions using a number line

◆ Comparing fractions to the landmarks 0, $\frac{1}{2}$, 1, and 2

◆ Ordering decimals and justifying their order through reasoning about representations and the meaning of the numbers

◆ Identifying decimal and fraction equivalents

As students' repertoire of fractions increases, they draw on their mental images of fractions and on their knowledge of fraction equivalencies and relationships to reason about fraction comparisons and ordering fractions on a number line. They draw on their knowledge of fraction equivalents as part of this reasoning ($\frac{5}{8}$ is more than $\frac{1}{2}$ because $\frac{1}{2} = \frac{4}{8}$ and $\frac{5}{8}$ is greater than $\frac{4}{8}$). They also use the relationship of fractions to landmarks, such as $\frac{1}{2}$ or 1, to determine which of two fractions is greater.

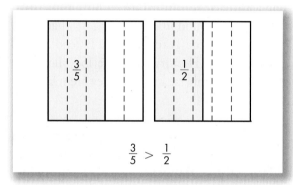

$$\frac{3}{5} > \frac{1}{2}$$

$\frac{3}{5}$ is more than $\frac{1}{2}$ because if you divide something into fifths, it only takes $2\frac{1}{2}$ of those pieces to make $\frac{1}{2}$.

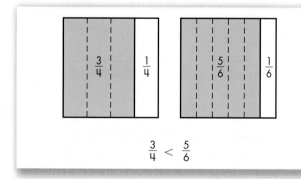

$$\frac{3}{4} < \frac{5}{6}$$

$\frac{3}{4}$ is $\frac{1}{4}$ less than 1. $\frac{5}{6}$ is $\frac{1}{6}$ less than 1. Since $\frac{1}{4}$ is greater than $\frac{1}{6}$, $\frac{3}{4}$ must be less than $\frac{5}{6}$.

In Investigation 2, as students reason about fraction comparisons, they develop and discuss a list of conjectures about fraction relationships (e.g., when the numerator is half the denominator, the fraction is equal to $\frac{1}{2}$; when the numerator is less than half the denominator, the fraction is less than $\frac{1}{2}$).

In their work with decimal fractions, students focus on multiples of 0.1 and multiples of 0.25 as they develop their understanding of the meaning of these numbers. By representing decimal fractions on rectangles divided into tenths and hundredths, they develop visual images of the relationships of these numbers; for example, that 0.9 is more than 0.4 and that 0.25 is more than 0.20.

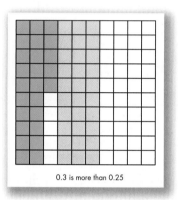

0.3 is more than 0.25

3 Computation with Rational Numbers Using representations to add rational numbers

Math Focus Points

◆ Using representations to add fractions that sum to 1

◆ Estimating sums of fractions

◆ Adding fractions with the same and related denominators (e.g., halves, fourths, and eighths; thirds and sixths)

◆ Estimating sums of decimal numbers

◆ Adding decimal numbers that are multiples of 0.1 and 0.25 (e.g., 2.3 + 3.25)

◆ Using representations to combine tenths and hundredths

Students add fractions and decimal fractions by drawing or visualizing representations of these numbers. They use pictures of groups of items or the area of rectangles as well as number lines. This unit does not concentrate on procedures for fraction or decimal computation but on using good number sense that is based on understandings of the quantities and their relationships. Students draw on their knowledge of fraction equivalencies and other relationships as they add fractions and decimals. For example, by the end of Grade 3, there were some combinations that students already "just knew" from representing fractions with pattern blocks and rectangles. Students continue to develop a repertoire of fraction equivalents and combinations as they find combinations of fractions that equal 1.

Although they are not formally learning about using common denominators to combine fractions, students are developing this idea as they use their knowledge of equivalents to add fractions such as $\frac{1}{2}$ and $\frac{3}{8}$ ("I know that $\frac{1}{2} = \frac{4}{8}$, so $\frac{4}{8} + \frac{3}{8} = \frac{7}{8}$").

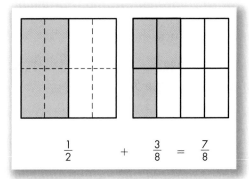

$$\frac{1}{2} \quad + \quad \frac{3}{8} \quad = \quad \frac{7}{8}$$

As they combine decimal amounts on rectangular grids, each representing one whole, they learn about adding tenths and decimals that have familiar fraction equivalents such as 0.25 and 0.75. Students have a great deal of experience with adding fractions in this unit and supporting their reasoning with visual models, but addition of fractions is not assessed until Grade 5. The major focus of this unit is on solidifying students' understanding of the meaning, order, and equivalencies of fractions and decimals.

Ten-Minute Math activities focus on

◆ Reading and writing numbers up to 10,000

◆ Adding multiples of 10 to, and subtracting multiples of 10 from 3- and 4-digit numbers

◆ Reading and writing decimal fractions and decimal numbers

◆ Adding tenths and hundredths to, and subtracting them from decimal fractions and decimal numbers

◆ Describing features of the data

◆ Interpreting and posing questions about the data

LOOKING FORWARD In two Grade 5 units, students work with percents, fractions, and decimals as different ways to represent the same quantities. They use equivalencies among these different forms of notation to develop flexibility in understanding and using them. Students order, add, and subtract fractions and order and add decimals by using representations with which they are already familiar (rectangles and number lines). They are also introduced to a new representation (a clock face) for fractions. Students learn about breaking apart fractions and decimals in ways that help them develop addition and subtraction strategies.

Technology Note

Using the *LogoPaths* Software If you are using the *LogoPaths* software this year, give students ongoing access to the computers **outside of math time** during this unit. *LogoPaths* Resource Masters (M1–M6) offer continued work with *Missing Measures* and *Steps* activities. Students can also continue to play *Mazes* and spend time working with the *Free Explore* option of the software. See **Part 5: Technology in** *Investigations* in *Implementing Investigations in Grade 4: Introducing and Managing the LogoPaths Software in Grade 4.*

Assessment

IN THIS UNIT

ONGOING ASSESSMENT: Observing Students at Work

The following sessions provide **Ongoing Assessment: Observing Students at Work** opportunities:

- **Session 1.1, pp. 27 and 30**
- **Session 1.2, p. 34**
- **Session 1.3, p. 40**
- **Session 1.4, pp. 44–45 and 46**
- **Session 1.5, p. 49**
- **Session 1.6, pp. 55 and 56**

- **Session 2.1, pp. 72–73**
- **Session 2.2, p. 75**
- **Session 2.3, p. 81**
- **Session 2.4, pp. 85 and 86**
- **Session 2.5, p. 92**
- **Session 3.1, p. 110**

- **Session 3.2, pp. 113 and 115**
- **Session 3.3, p. 119**
- **Session 3.4, p. 124**
- **Session 3.5, p. 129**

WRITING OPPORTUNITIES

The following sessions have **writing** opportunities for students to explain their mathematical thinking:

- **Session 1.5, p. 50**
  M12, Assessment: Identifying and Comparing Fractions

- **Session 2.2, p. 75**
  Student Activity Book, p. 31

- **Session 2.3, p. 82**
  Student Activity Book, p. 35

- **Session 2.6, p. 95**
  M23, Assessment: Comparing Fractions

- **Session 3.5, p. 129**
  Student Activity Book, pp. 57–58

- **Session 3.7, p. 136**
  M31, End-of-Unit Assessment

PORTFOLIO OPPORTUNITIES

The following sessions have work appropriate for a **portfolio:**

- **Session 1.5, p. 50**
  M12, Assessment: Identifying and Comparing Fractions

- **Session 1.6, pp. 54–55**
  Student Activity Book, pp. 19–21

- **Session 2.6, p. 95**
  M23, Assessment: Comparing Fractions

- **Session 3.5, p. 129**
  Student Activity Book, pp. 57–58

- **Session 3.7, p. 136**
  M31, End-of-Unit Assessment

Assessing the Benchmarks

Observing students as they engage in conversation about their ideas is a primary means to assess their mathematical understanding. Consider all of your students' work, not just the written assessments. See the chart below for suggestions about key activities to observe.

Benchmarks in This Unit	Key Activities to Observe	Assessment
1. Identify fractional parts of an area.	**Session 1.1:** Finding Fourths and Eighths **Session 1.2:** Finding Thirds and Sixths **Sessions 2.1 and 2.2:** Making Fraction Cards	**Session 1.5 Assessment Activity:** Identifying and Comparing Fractions, Problem 1
2. Identify fractional parts of a group (of objects, people, etc.).	**Session 1.3:** Fractions of 24 **Sessions 1.4 and 1.6:** Story Problems About a Class	**Session 1.5 Assessment Activity:** Identifying and Comparing Fractions, Problem 2 **Session 3.7 Assessment Activity:** End-of-Unit Assessment, Problem 1
3. Read, write, and interpret fraction notation.	**Sessions 1.4 and 1.6:** Story Problems About a Class **Sessions 2.3, 2.5, and 2.6:** *Capture Fractions* **Sessions 2.5 and 2.6:** Fractions on a Number Line	**Session 1.5 Assessment Activity:** Identifying and Comparing Fractions, Problems 1, 2, and 3 **Session 2.6 Assessment Activity:** Comparing Fractions
4. Order fractions with like and unlike denominators.	**Sessions 2.3, 2.5, and 2.6:** *Capture Fractions* **Session 2.5 and 2.6:** Fractions on a Number Line	**Session 1.5 Assessment Activity:** Identifying and Comparing Fractions, Problem 3 **Session 2.6 Assessment Activity:** Comparing Fractions **Session 3.7 Assessment Activity:** End-of-Unit Assessment, Problems 1 and 2
5. Read, write, and interpret decimal fractions in tenths and hundredths.	**Sessions 3.2, 3.5, and 3.6:** *Decimal Compare* **Sessions 3.3, 3.5, and 3.6:** *Fill Two*	**Session 3.7 Assessment Activity:** End-of-Unit Assessment, Problem 3

Relating the Mathematical Emphases to the Benchmarks

Mathematical Emphases	Benchmarks
Rational Numbers Understanding the meaning of fractions and decimal fractions	1, 2, 3, and 5
Rational Numbers Comparing the values of fractions and decimal fractions	3 and 4
Computation with Rational Numbers Using representations to add rational numbers	

Ten-Minute Math

Ten-Minute Math offers practice and review of key concepts for this grade level. These daily activities, to be done in ten minutes outside of math class, are introduced in a unit and repeated throughout the grade. Specific directions for the day's activity are provided in each session. For the full description and variations of each classroom activity, see *Implementing Investigations in Grade 4*.

Activity	Introduced	Full Description of Activity and Its Variations
Practicing Place Value	Unit 5, Session 1.3	*Implementing Investigations in Grade 4*
Quick Survey	Unit 2, Session 1.1	*Implementing Investigations in Grade 4*

Practicing Place Value

Students practice reading, writing, and saying numbers up to 10,000, including decimal fractions and decimal numbers. They add and subtract multiples of one tenth and multiples of 10, and examine how these operations increase or decrease the values of the digits in each place.

Math Focus Points

◆ Reading and writing numbers up to 10,000

◆ Adding multiples of 10 to, and subtracting multiples of 10 from 3- and 4-digit numbers

◆ Reading and writing decimal fractions and decimal numbers

◆ Adding tenths and hundredths to, and subtracting them from decimal fractions and decimal numbers

Quick Survey

Students collect, display, describe, and interpret data about themselves or something they can observe easily. Students describe what they can tell from the data, generate some new questions and, if appropriate, make predictions about what will happen the next time they collect the same data.

Math Focus Points

◆ Describing features of the data

◆ Interpreting and posing questions about the data

Practice and Review

Practice and review play a critical role in the *Investigations* program. The following components and features are available to provide regular reinforcement of key mathematical concepts and procedures.

Books	Features	In This Unit . . .
Curriculum Unit	**Ten-Minute Math** offers practice and review of key concepts for this grade level. These daily activities, to be done in ten minutes outside of math class, are introduced in a unit and repeated throughout the grade. Specific directions for the day's activity are provided in each session. For the full description and variations of each classroom activity, see *Implementing Investigations in Grade 4*.	• **All sessions**
Student Activity Book	**Daily Practice** pages in the *Student Activity Book* provide one of three types of written practice: **reinforcement** of the content of the unit, **ongoing review,** or **enrichment** opportunities. Some Daily Practice pages will also have Ongoing Review items with multiple-choice problems similar to those on standardized tests.	• **All sessions**
	Homework pages in the *Student Activity Book* are an extension of the work done in class. At times they help students prepare for upcoming activities.	• **Session 1.1** • **Session 2.3** • **Session 1.3** • **Session 2.5** • **Session 1.4** • **Session 3.1** • **Session 1.5** • **Session 3.2** • **Session 2.1** • **Session 3.4**
Student Math Handbook	**Math Words and Ideas** in the *Student Math Handbook* are pages that summarize key words and ideas. Most Words and Ideas pages have at least one exercise.	• **Student Math Handbook, pp. 8–9, 13–15, 53–71**
	Games pages are found in a section of the *Student Math Handbook*.	• **Student Math Handbook, pp. G1, G4, G7**

Supporting the Range of Learners

Sessions	1.1	1.2	1.4	1.5	1.6	2.1	2.2	2.3	2.4	2.5	2.6	3.1	3.2	3.3	3.4	3.5	3.7
Intervention	●	●	●	●	●	●	●	●	●	●		●	●	●	●	●	●
Extension	●	●	●	●				●		●			●	●	●	●	
ELL	●	●	●		●						●	●	●				

Intervention

Adjustments to the activities are provided to support students who may need additional practice or who may benefit from alternate teaching strategies.

Extension

Adjustments to the activities are provided to support students who may finish early or who may be ready for more challenging or enriching activities.

English Language Learners (ELL)

In this unit, students focus on the meaning, order, and equivalencies of fractions and decimals. English Language Learners will need to practice the names of fractions and decimals. Make a chart of numerical fractions and their corresponding names for English Language Learners to refer to throughout the unit. Add decimal fractions and their corresponding names as you begin the work with decimals.

Before beginning the work in this unit, English Language Learners may need to review expressions that are used to make comparisons, such as *greater (than), more (than), less (than), same (as), equal (to)*, and *equivalent*. When talking about fractional and decimal relationships, students also need to distinguish between the terms "how many" and "how much." When modeling proper usage of "how many" and "how much," you can show two blue cubes and three red cubes separated. Ask: "How many cubes are red?" or "How many cubes are blue?" Then put the cubes together in a train and ask: "How much of the train is red? ($\frac{3}{5}$). You can use the words *how many* when you want to identify the number of items. You can use the words *how much* when you want to identify a part of a whole." A t-chart could be created listing instances of using "how many" and "how much."

During activities, help English Language Learners develop their ability to express ideas in English. This will give you the opportunity to model the language of fractions and decimals in the context of the concrete materials or representations used in the sessions.

To help English Language Learners participate more fully in class discussions, meet with them beforehand when possible to preview the questions you plan to ask. By giving them the chance to formulate and practice answers ahead of time, you can assess their understanding of the math content and provide them with the language they may require.

Working with the Range of Learners: Classroom Cases is a set of episodes written by teachers that focuses on meeting the needs of the range of learners in the classroom. In the first section, *Setting up the Mathematical Community,* teachers write about how they create a supportive and productive learning environment in their classrooms. In the next section, *Accommodations for Learning,* teachers focus on specific modifications they make to meet the needs of some of their learners. In the last section, *Language and Representation,* teachers share how they help students use representations and develop language to investigate and express mathematical ideas. The questions at the end of each case provide a starting point for your own reflection or for discussion with colleagues. See *Implementing Investigations in Grade 4* for this set of episodes.

Mathematical Emphases

Rational Numbers Understanding the meaning of fractions and decimal fractions

Math Focus Points

◆ Finding fractional parts of a rectangular area

◆ Interpreting the meaning of the numerator and the denominator of a fraction

◆ Finding fractional parts of a group (of objects, people, etc.)

◆ Writing, reading, and applying fraction notation

Rational Numbers Comparing the values of fractions and decimal fractions

Math Focus Points

◆ Identifying relationships between unit fractions when one denominator is a multiple of the other (e.g., halves and fourths, thirds and sixths)

◆ Identifying equivalent fractions

◆ Comparing the same fractional parts of different-sized wholes

Computation with Rational Numbers Using representations to add rational numbers

Math Focus Points

◆ Using representations to add fractions that sum to 1

◆ Adding fractions with the same and related denominators (e.g., halves, fourths, and eighths; thirds and sixths)

◆ Estimating sums of fractions

Parts of Rectangles

	Student Activity Book	Student Math Handbook	Professional Development: Read Ahead of Time	
SESSION 1.1 p. 24				
Fractions of an Area: Halves, Fourths, and Eighths Students identify halves, fourths, and eighths of a 4 × 6 rectangle and discuss how they know that each fractional part is $\frac{1}{2}$, $\frac{1}{4}$, $\frac{2}{4}$, $\frac{3}{4}$, or $\frac{1}{8}$ of the whole rectangle.	1–3	53–54	• **Mathematics in This Unit**, p. 10 • **Part 4: Ten-Minute Math** in *Implementing Investigations in Grade 4:* Practicing Place Value	
SESSION 1.2 p. 32				
Fractions of an Area: Thirds and Sixths Students find thirds and sixths of a 4 × 6 rectangle. They also consider what part of the rectangle is $\frac{2}{3}$, $\frac{2}{6}$, $\frac{3}{6}$, or $\frac{4}{6}$ and talk about how they know by referring to equal parts of a whole. They discuss the relationship between $\frac{1}{3}$ and $\frac{1}{6}$.	5	53–54, 59	• **Teacher Note:** Why Are Fractions Difficult? Developing Meaning for Fractions, p. 139 • **Teacher Note:** Visualizing Fraction Equivalencies, p. 141	
SESSION 1.3 p. 37				
Fractions of Groups of Things Students solve problems in which they find fractional parts of a group of 24 objects.	6–10	55		
SESSION 1.4 p. 41				
Same Parts, Different Wholes Students compare the same fractional parts of different-sized wholes. They solve problems that involve fractions of the area of a rectangle and fractions of a group of things.	11–15	63		
SESSION 1.5 p. 47				
Assessment: Identifying and Comparing Fractions Students find combinations of fractions that equal one whole rectangle. They are assessed on their ability to identify thirds and sixths of a 5 × 12 rectangle and their understanding of the relationship between $\frac{1}{8}$ and $\frac{1}{4}$.	17–18	54–57	• **Teacher Note:** Assessment: Identifying and Comparing Fractions, p. 143	

Materials to Gather	Materials to Prepare
• **T64, 4 × 6 Rectangles** 🖥 • **T65, $\frac{1}{4}$ of a 4 × 6 Rectangle** 🖥 • **Colored pencils or crayons** (as needed)	• **M1–M6, *LogoPaths Missing Measures* and *Steps*** Make copies for ongoing use of the computer with the *LogoPaths* software. (1 per student; optional) • **M7, 4 × 6 Rectangles** Make copies. (Start out by making 4 copies per student and make additional copies as needed. The 4 × 6 Rectangles will be used throughout the unit.) • **M9–M10, Family Letter** Make copies. (1 per student)
• **M7, 4 × 6 Rectangles** (from Session 1.1; 2 per student) • **T64, 4 × 6 Rectangles** 🖥 • **Colored pencils or crayons** (as needed)	• **Chart paper** Title a sheet of chart paper "Fractions That Are Equal." Students begin this list in this session and add to it throughout the unit.
• **M7, 4 × 6 Rectangles** (from Session 1.1; 2 per student) • **T64, 4 × 6 Rectangles** 🖥 • **Connecting cubes** (as needed) • **Colored pencils or crayons** (as needed)	• **Chart paper** Write on the board or a sheet of chart paper the problem shown on page 38.
• **M7, 4 × 6 Rectangles** (from Session 1.1; 2 per student) • **T66, 5 × 12 Rectangles** 🖥 • **Connecting cubes** (as needed) • **Colored pencils or crayons** (as needed)	• **M11, 5 × 12 Rectangles** Make copies. (Start out by making 5 copies per student and make additional copies as needed. The 5 × 12 Rectangles will be used during the rest of the investigation.) • **M13–M14, Family Letter** Make copies. (1 per student) • **Chart paper** Title a sheet of chart paper "Fractions to Find on the 5 × 12 Rectangles." Post the list of fractions that students will use to find parts of the 5 × 12 Rectangle. See illustration, p. 44.
• **M11, 5 × 12 Rectangles** (from Session 1.4; 1 per student) • **T66, 5 × 12 Rectangles** 🖥 • **Colored pencils or crayons** (as needed)	• **M12, Assessment: Identifying and Comparing Fractions** Make copies. (1 per student) • **Chart paper** Title a sheet of chart paper "Combinations of Fractions That Equal 1." Students begin this list in this session and add to it throughout the unit. See illustration, p. 49.

🖥 Overhead Transparency

Parts of Rectangles, *continued*

	Student Activity Book	Student Math Handbook	Professional Development: Read Ahead of Time	
SESSION 1.6 p. 52				
Combinations That Equal 1 Students solve problems about adding fractions with like and unlike denominators, posed both in story contexts and just with numbers. They continue to represent fractional parts of a rectangle and find combinations of fractions that equal one whole rectangle.	19–24	62	• **Dialogue Box:** Finding Combinations That Equal 1, p. 164	
SESSION 1.7 p. 58				
Adding Fractions Students estimate whether a fraction sum is greater than or less than 1. They continue Math Workshop activities that focus on adding fractions with like and unlike denominators and finding fractional parts of rectangles.	19–23, 25	62		

Materials to Gather	Materials to Prepare
• **M7, 4 × 6 Rectangles** (from Session 1.1; as needed) • **M11, 5 × 12 Rectangles** (from Session 1.4; as needed) • **T64, 4 × 6 Rectangles** 🖳 • **T66, 5 × 12 Rectangles** 🖳 • **Chart:** "Combinations of Fractions That Equal 1" (from Session 1.5) • **Counters** (as needed) • **Colored pencils or crayons** (as needed) • **Connecting cubes** (as needed)	• **M15, 10 × 10 Squares** Make copies. (2 per student and additional copies as needed) • **Chart paper** Title a sheet of chart paper "Fractions to Find on the 10 × 10 Squares." Post the list of fractions that students will use to find parts of the 10 × 10 Squares. See example, p. 57. (optional)
• **M7, 4 × 6 Rectangles** (from Session 1.1; as needed) • **M11, 5 × 12 Rectangles** (from Session 1.4; as needed) • **M15, 10 × 10 Squares** (from Session 1.6; 1 per student) • **Chart:** "Combinations of Fractions That Equal 1" (from Session 1.5) • **Chart:** "Fractions to Find on the 10 × 10 Squares" (from Session 1.6; optional) • **Counters** (as needed)	

🖳 Overhead Transparency

Fractions of an Area: Halves, Fourths, and Eighths

Math Focus Points

◆ Finding fractional parts of a rectangular area

◆ Interpreting the meaning of the numerator and the denominator of a fraction

Vocabulary

fraction
denominator
numerator

Today's Plan		Materials
ACTIVITY ❶ Introducing Halves and Fourths 30 MIN CLASS INDIVIDUALS		• *Student Activity Book,* p. 1 • T64 ; T65
ACTIVITY ❷ Finding Fourths and Eighths  30 MIN INDIVIDUALS PAIRS		• *Student Activity Book,* p. 1 • M7* (as needed); T64 • Colored pencils or crayons (as needed)
SESSION FOLLOW-UP ❸ Daily Practice and Homework		• *Student Activity Book,* pp. 2–3 • *Student Math Handbook,* pp. 53–54 • M9–M10, Family Letter*

*See *Materials to Prepare,* p. 21.

*[handwritten] Talk about what they did in 3rd grade. * See packet*
[handwritten] Relate to Cutting brownies

Ten-Minute Math

Practicing Place Value Say "eight hundred seventy-four" and have students practice writing the number. Make sure all students can read, write, and say this number correctly. Ask students to solve these problems mentally, if possible:

• What is 874 + 30? 874 + 40? 874 + 50? 874 + 100? 874 + 200? 874 + 300?

Write each answer on the board. Ask students to compare each sum with 874. Which places have the same digits? Which do not? Why? If time remains, pose additional similar problems using these numbers: 459 and 503.

ACTIVITY

Introducing Halves and Fourths

Explain to students that for the next few weeks they will be learning about fractions. They will be dividing up rectangles, finding fractions of groups, putting fractions in order, and adding fractions.

Display the transparency 4 × 6 Rectangles (T64). Cover all of the rectangles except one. Briefly review how to identify $\frac{1}{2}$ of a rectangle with students.

Imagine that this rectangle is a sandwich. I want to eat half now and save half for later. I'm going to cut it like this.

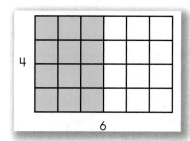

What fraction of the rectangle is this shaded piece? What fraction is the other piece?

Label each piece $\frac{1}{2}$ after students agree.

What if I wanted to eat only $\frac{1}{4}$ of this sandwich? Turn to *Student Activity Book* page 1 and find a few different ways to show $\frac{1}{4}$ of the rectangle.

Explain that for this activity, each fourth must be a whole piece, not two or more disconnected pieces.

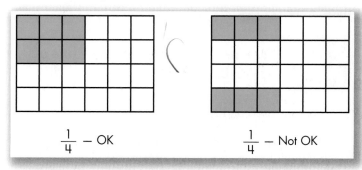

$\frac{1}{4}$ — OK $\frac{1}{4}$ — Not OK

Allow students a few minutes to show one fourth in different ways on *Student Activity Book* page 1. As they work, ask them how they know that their piece is exactly one fourth of the whole rectangle.❶

---

❶ **Measuring Area in Square Units** Remind students about the work they did measuring area earlier in the year. Area is measured in square units. In this case, the units are square centimeters. When you talk about the area of these rectangles, use the words *square units* or *square centimeters* so that students hear these terms used correctly in context.

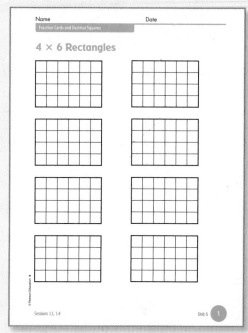

▲ **Student Activity Book, p. 1; Resource Masters, M7; T64**

Teaching Note

❷ **Cutting and Folding** Some students may be able to divide the rectangles into fractional parts by drawing and reasoning about the equal areas, saying for example, "I know that each piece is one fourth because there are four pieces and each one has 6 squares." Some students can benefit from folding or cutting to physically match the pieces to each other. Provide loose copies of 4 × 6 Rectangles (M7) and encourage students to fold and/or cut during the first few sessions of this Investigation to see whether they have equal pieces.

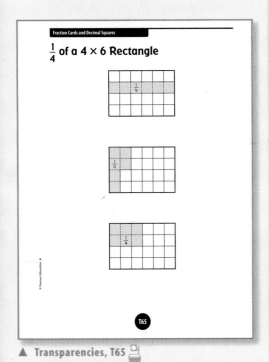

▲ Transparencies, T65

Students might say:

 "I know that the whole rectangle has 24 squares and there are four 6s in 24. My fourth has 6 squares in it, so I know that it is $\frac{1}{4}$."

 "I can fold the rectangle in half and I can see that both pieces are equal. Then I can fold it in half again and I can see that all 4 pieces are equal. If there are 4 equal pieces, one of those pieces is $\frac{1}{4}$."

Often students explain that they know that a piece is a particular fraction because it "looks like it." Explain to students that it is sometimes very difficult to determine the size of a fractional part just by looking and that they should find some other way to prove that a piece is exactly $\frac{1}{4}$.

What if someone else looks at it and doesn't think that it looks like one fourth of the sandwich? How could you convince them that it is one fourth?❷

Show $\frac{1}{4}$ of a 4 × 6 Rectangle (T65) on the overhead projector. These are a few fourths that students often find.

These all look different, but they are all $\frac{1}{4}$ of the whole rectangle. Who can explain how you know that these are all $\frac{1}{4}$?

Students might say:

 "They all have six squares."

 "I can see that they are each one of four equal pieces."

Using the second example on transparency T65, ask students to name the fraction of the rectangle that is not shaded.

We agree that this is $\frac{1}{4}$. What fraction of the whole rectangle is the rest of the space?

Point to the rest of the rectangle, or shade it in a different color.

Allow students a few minutes to think with a partner about the size of the rest of the rectangle. Then collect ideas and ask students to explain their thinking.

Students might say:

 "The unshaded part is $\frac{3}{4}$ because 3 more of the $\frac{1}{4}$ shapes can fit in that space. $\frac{1}{4}$ plus $\frac{1}{4}$ plus $\frac{1}{4}$ is $\frac{3}{4}$."

 "The large part is $\frac{3}{4}$ because there are 4 quarters in one whole. One quarter ($\frac{1}{4}$) is shaded, so there are $\frac{3}{4}$ left unshaded and that makes 1 whole all together."

 "I know that there are 6 squares in $\frac{1}{4}$. I counted 18 squares in the unshaded piece. Three 6s are 18, so the rest is $\frac{3}{4}$."

If I share this sandwich among four people, what fraction of the sandwich would each person get? What fraction of the sandwich would two people get? (Some students may notice here that $\frac{2}{4}$ is the same as $\frac{1}{2}$.) If three people take their shares, how many fourths is that?

As students share answers, record each fraction on the board. Summarize by pointing out the following:

The number on the bottom of the fraction shows the total number of pieces that make up the whole. That number is called the *denominator*. The number on the top shows how many of those pieces we are talking about. That number is called the *numerator*.❸

ONGOING ASSESSMENT: Observing Students at Work

Students identify $\frac{1}{4}$ and $\frac{3}{4}$ of a 4 × 6 rectangle.

- **Can students find $\frac{1}{4}$ of the 4 × 6 rectangle?**

- **Can they explain how they know that it is $\frac{1}{4}$, either by demonstrating that it is composed of 6 out of 24 squares or by showing that it is 1 of 4 equal pieces?**

- **Can students identify $\frac{3}{4}$ of a rectangle?** Can they explain the meaning of $\frac{3}{4}$?

Math Note

❸ **Congruence** Students studied *congruence* in the 2-D Geometry unit *Size, Shape, and Symmetry*. They worked with the idea that congruent shapes have the same area, but that shapes with the same area are not necessarily congruent. As they work on identifying fractions, they should understand that the same-sized fraction of a whole can be shaped differently. While this idea should be familiar to students, there may be some students who need to examine it again. You can ask these students to divide one whole into four equal parts that are all differently shaped. Ask them to explain how they know that each of the pieces is $\frac{1}{4}$ of the whole.

DIFFERENTIATION: Supporting the Range of Learners

Intervention If some students are having a difficult time identifying one fourth of the rectangle, help students understand that one fourth is one piece of *four equal pieces* of the whole rectangle by using the sharing context. "If I want to share this sandwich among four people equally, how could I cut it? How would I know that we were each getting the same amount?" Determining whether a picture represents one fourth can be easier than creating a picture (that shows one fourth) yourself. Therefore, on the transparency 4 × 6 Rectangles (T64), you may want to show one fourth on some rectangles, and areas that are not one fourth on others. Ask the student to determine which show one fourth of the rectangle and which do not. For example, show these representations.

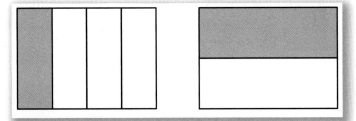

ELL While English Language Learners may have developed facility with the names of whole numbers, making the transition to naming fractions can be challenging. For example, students will need practice in naming the 4 they see in the fraction $\frac{1}{4}$ as a *fourth* rather than *four*. As you write fractions, orally model how the fraction is read. Ask students to identify the part of the fraction that says fourths, sixths, eighths, etc. Then as the students write fractions, ask them to say them orally.

ACTIVITY

30 MIN INDIVIDUALS PAIRS

2 Finding Fourths and Eighths

For the rest of this session, students find fourths and eighths of a 4 × 6 rectangle. Draw the following on the board or overhead projector:

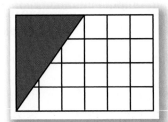

Suppose that someone said that this shaded piece is $\frac{1}{4}$ of the whole rectangle and the rest of the rectangle is $\frac{3}{4}$. Do you think this is correct? Talk about this with a partner.

Allow students a few minutes to think about this question and then ask for some ideas. As students share their ideas, encourage them to explain their reasoning clearly. Saying "it looks like $\frac{3}{4}$" is not enough of an explanation.

Students might say:

 "I can see that four of those triangles can fit into the whole rectangle. So one of those pieces is $\frac{1}{4}$ and the other three are $\frac{3}{4}$. Two of them would be $\frac{2}{4}$."

 "If you cut the whole thing in half, you can get two of those triangles out of each half, so there are four triangles. So three of them is $\frac{3}{4}$ of the whole sandwich."

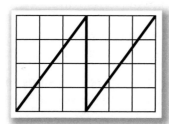

So $\frac{1}{4}$ of this rectangle plus $\frac{3}{4}$ of this rectangle equals the whole rectangle. ❹

Record $\frac{1}{4} + \frac{3}{4} = 1$ on the board.

Explain to students that for the rest of the class, they will be finding and labeling fourths on their 4×6 rectangles.

If students complete *Student Activity Book* page 1, give them a copy of 4×6 Rectangles (M7).

Use your 4×6 rectangles to shade in and label the following fractions: $\frac{1}{4}$, $\frac{2}{4}$, and $\frac{3}{4}$. See whether you can divide each rectangle into fourths differently as you are finding ways to make these fractional parts. If you have time, find more than one way to make each fractional part.

As students work on this, collect a few examples for the class to look at by asking some students to draw the way they are showing fractional parts on the rectangles on the transparency 4×6 Rectangles (T64).

Math Note

❹ **Reasoning About the Triangular Fourths** This example is designed to expand students' ideas about how to create a fourth of the rectangle. It also supports them in reasoning about the equal areas of the pieces, rather than relying only on counting squares. When students realize that a fourth of the 4×6 rectangle contains six squares, they can easily create different shapes of fourths with any combination of six contiguous squares. In this example, it is not easy to count squares, so students must focus on the relationship of the part to the whole and the equal areas of the four parts.

When there are 15 minutes left in class, challenge students to see whether they can find and shade in $\frac{1}{8}$ of a 4 × 6 rectangle.

You will see on the overhead some examples of fourths of a 4 × 6 rectangle. Now I want you to find $\frac{1}{8}$ of the same rectangle. Think about sharing this same sandwich among eight people. Will each piece, each eighth, be bigger or smaller than $\frac{1}{2}$ and $\frac{1}{4}$?

Work to find a few examples of $\frac{1}{8}$ of the sandwich.

Examples of eighths include the following:

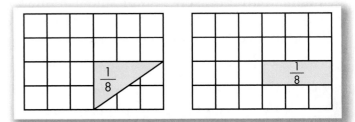

ONGOING ASSESSMENT: Observing Students at Work

Students find fourths and eighths of a 4 × 6 rectangle.

- **Can students identify $\frac{1}{4}$, $\frac{2}{4}$, $\frac{3}{4}$, and $\frac{1}{8}$ of a rectangle?** Can they divide the rectangle into fourths in different ways?

- **How do students use relationships among halves, fourths, and eighths to determine the size of fractional parts?** For example, do they know that $\frac{2}{4}$ of the rectangle is the same amount as $\frac{1}{2}$ of the rectangle? That $\frac{1}{4}$ plus $\frac{1}{2}$ of the rectangle are $\frac{3}{4}$ of the rectangle? That $\frac{1}{4}$ is half of $\frac{1}{2}$?

- **Can they explain how they know that they have shaded in $\frac{1}{4}$, $\frac{2}{4}$, $\frac{3}{4}$, or $\frac{1}{8}$?**

As students are working, ask the following questions:

- How do you know that this piece you colored in is exactly $\frac{1}{4}$, $\frac{2}{4}$, $\frac{3}{4}$, or $\frac{1}{8}$?

- Can you use this fourth to help you find $\frac{1}{8}$? How are these two fractions related?

- Do you know the fractional part that is not shaded? ($\frac{1}{2}$, $\frac{3}{4}$, $\frac{7}{8}$)

DIFFERENTIATION: Supporting the Range of Learners

Intervention Pair a student who is having difficulty with a student who has found several examples of fourths or eighths. Suggest that the students take turns explaining why they know that a shaded area is $\frac{1}{4}$ or $\frac{1}{8}$. When they agree that the shaded area accurately represents the fraction, the students may copy the fraction shapes onto their page.

Extension For additional challenge, ask students to shade in and label multiples of $\frac{1}{8}$ (e.g., $\frac{2}{8}, \frac{3}{8}, \frac{4}{8}$, and so on). Some students may notice equivalent fractions. If so, ask them to record them in the form of equations (e.g., $\frac{4}{8} = \frac{1}{2}, \frac{3}{4} = \frac{6}{8}$).

Students can also be challenged to determine what fraction of the rectangle the shaded part in the figure below is.

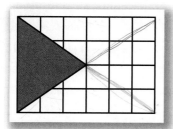

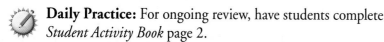

SESSION FOLLOW-UP

3 Daily Practice and Homework

Daily Practice: For ongoing review, have students complete *Student Activity Book* page 2.

Homework: Students identify halves, fourths, and eighths on 4×6 rectangles on *Student Activity Book* page 3.

Student Math Handbook: Students and families may use *Student Math Handbook* pages 53–54 for reference and review. See pages 170–176 in the back of this unit.

Family Letter: Send home copies of the Family Letter (M9–M10) to introduce students' families to the content of this unit.

▲ Student Activity Book, p. 2

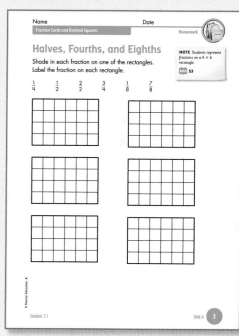

▲ Student Activity Book, p. 3

Fractions of an Area: Thirds and Sixths

Math Focus Points

◆ Finding fractional parts of a rectangular area

◆ Identifying relationships between unit fractions when one denominator is a multiple of the other (e.g., halves and fourths, thirds and sixths)

◆ Identifying equivalent fractions

Vocabulary

thirds
sixths

Today's Plan

	Materials
ACTIVITY **1 Finding Thirds and Sixths** 40 MIN INDIVIDUALS PAIRS	• M7 (from Session 1.1); T64 • Colored pencils or crayons (as needed)
DISCUSSION **2 How Are Thirds and Sixths Related?** 20 MIN CLASS PAIRS	• T64 • Chart: "Fractions That Are Equal"*
SESSION FOLLOW-UP **3 Daily Practice**	• *Student Activity Book,* p. 5 • *Student Math Handbook,* pp. 53–54, 59

*See *Materials to Prepare,* p. 21.

Ten-Minute Math

Practicing Place Value Write 305 on the board and have students practice saying it. Make sure that all students can read, write, and say this number correctly. Ask students to solve these problems mentally, if possible:

• What is 305 + 50? 305 + 60? 305 + 70? 305 + 500? 305 + 600? 305 + 700?

Write each answer on the board. Ask students to compare each sum with 305. Which places have the same digits? Which do not? Why? If time remains, pose additional similar problems with the numbers 826 and 691.

ACTIVITY

Finding Thirds and Sixths

40 MIN INDIVIDUALS PAIRS

Distribute two more copies of 4 × 6 Rectangles (M7) to each student.

Today you are going to split some of these rectangular "sandwiches" into thirds. If three people share this sandwich equally, what fraction of the sandwich will one person get? Do you think that one third of this rectangle will be more or less than one half?

Allow students a minute to talk to a partner and explain what they think. Then solicit a few responses from the group.❶ ❷

Some students may already be able to articulate an important idea about fractions that all are expected to understand by the end of the unit.

Students might say:

"I know that $\frac{1}{3}$ will be smaller than $\frac{1}{2}$ because if you divide a sandwich in half, you are sharing it between two people. If you divide a sandwich into thirds, you are sharing it among three people. It's the same sandwich, but you're going to get a smaller piece. The more people that share the same thing, the less each person will get."

Ask students to help you show one third on one of the rectangles on the transparency 4 × 6 Rectangles (T64).

We shaded one third of this rectangle. What fractional part of the rectangle is not shaded? In other words, if you eat $\frac{1}{3}$ of the sandwich, how much of the sandwich is left?

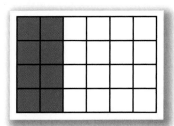

Collect some ideas, but continue to ask questions such as these. Have students work for about 20 minutes, finding ways to share fractional parts that involve thirds and then sixths. Students should find several ways to show $\frac{1}{3}$ and $\frac{1}{6}$. If they have time, they can also show $\frac{2}{3}$, $\frac{2}{6}$, $\frac{3}{6}$, and $\frac{4}{6}$.

Draw some of the students' ways of showing thirds and sixths on the transparency 4 × 6 Rectangles (T64) to show during the discussion.

ONGOING ASSESSMENT: Observing Students at Work

- **Can students identify $\frac{1}{3}$ and $\frac{1}{6}$ of a 4 × 6 rectangle?**

- **Can students identify $\frac{1}{3}$ as one of three equal parts of a whole (and $\frac{1}{6}$ as 1 out of 6 equal parts)?**

- **Can students identify fractions of the whole with numerators larger than 1 (e.g., $\frac{2}{3}, \frac{3}{6}$)?**

- **Can students use correct fraction notation for the parts they identify?**

As students are working, ask the following questions:

- How do you know that part of the rectangle is $[\frac{1}{3}, \frac{1}{6}]$?

- Can you show me $\frac{2}{3}$ or $\frac{3}{3}$? Can you show me $\frac{2}{6}$ or $\frac{3}{6}$?

- If the shaded piece is $\frac{2}{3}$, what fraction is the rest of the rectangle? How do you know?

DIFFERENTIATION: Supporting the Range of Learners

Intervention Students who have difficulty visualizing thirds of a region may find it easier to start by finding one third of 24 objects and then counting out that number of squares on the rectangle. You may also pair a student who is having difficulty with one who quickly splits the regions into thirds and ask the student who has difficulty to check that the regions are equal.

Extension Students who quickly make thirds and sixths and can explain clearly how they know what fraction represents a part of the rectangle can work with twelfths. These students can also divide a rectangle into a combination of thirds, sixths, and twelfths, being sure to label each fraction.

DISCUSSION

2 How Are Thirds and Sixths Related?

20 MIN   CLASS   PAIRS

Math Focus Points for Discussion

◆ Identifying relationships between unit fractions when one denominator is a multiple of the other (e.g., halves and fourths, thirds and sixths)

Show the examples of students' thirds and sixths that you collected on the transparency. Ask students to explain how they are sure that parts of the rectangle are correctly labeled as $\frac{1}{3}$ or $\frac{1}{6}$. Then focus the discussion by asking the following:

Did anyone use the way you showed $\frac{1}{3}$ of the rectangle to find $\frac{1}{6}$ of the rectangle?

Show one or two examples of how students did this. For example, a student may show these two representations of $\frac{1}{3}$ and $\frac{1}{6}$ to show how dividing $\frac{1}{3}$ into two equal parts resulted in sixths:

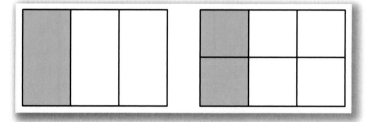

Referring to a drawing like the one above from a student or one that you draw on the board, ask about the relationship between one third and two sixths.

Many of you drew thirds that look like this [point to the shaded third in the diagram] and sixths that look like this [point to a shaded sixth]. What can you say about $\frac{1}{3}$ and $\frac{2}{6}$? How do you know?

After hearing some of the students' ideas, write "$\frac{1}{3} = \frac{2}{6}$?" on the board. Allow students a few minutes to talk with a partner and find a way to explain whether $\frac{1}{3} = \frac{2}{6}$. Then ask them to share their ideas. Listen for explanations that focus on the relationship between thirds and sixths.

Students might say:

 "I noticed that if I cut one of my thirds in half, I got two sixths. Each sixth is half as big as $\frac{1}{3}$."

 "I noticed that in one whole there are 6 sixths and 3 thirds, so there are twice as many sixths. So each third equals 2 of the sixths."

If students are convinced that $\frac{1}{3} = \frac{2}{6}$, write this equation on the chart you prepared, "Fractions That Are Equal." If they are not yet sure, wait until students have done further work on this idea. Then ask students to consider the following:

Teaching Note

❸ **"Fractions That Are Equal" Chart** Refer to this chart often as students use equivalent fractions in their work. Students should be developing a repertoire of *fraction facts*—equivalencies of familiar fractions—that they can use to solve problems. Encourage students to add to this chart, and add to it yourself, especially during class discussions when students use equivalent fractions as they reason about a problem.

Professional Development

❹ **Teacher Note:** Visualizing Fraction Equivalencies, p. 141

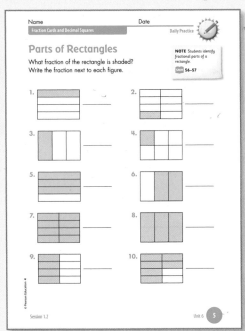

▲ **Student Activity Book, p. 5**

What fraction is equal to $\frac{2}{3}$? What about $\frac{3}{6}$? Work with a partner for a few minutes and see whether you can find any other fractions that are equal to these two fractions.

Fractions That Are Equal

$$\frac{1}{3} = \frac{2}{6}$$
$$\frac{2}{3} = \frac{4}{6}$$
$$\frac{3}{6} = \frac{1}{2}$$

Explain to students that they will be thinking more about equivalent fractions over the next couple of weeks. They will add to this list of equivalent fractions as the work in the unit continues. Keep the chart posted throughout the unit. ❸ ❹

DIFFERENTIATION: Supporting the Range of Learners

ELL After the chart is posted, bring students up to the chart along with the rectangles they have been using. To check for understanding of the term *equivalent fractions,* connect the word *equivalent* to the word *equal* and ask how the terms are similar. Then ask English Language Learners to use their rectangles to show you *equivalent fractions.* For example,

Show me $\frac{1}{3}$ of your rectangle. Can you show me a fraction that's *equivalent* to $\frac{1}{3}$? Show me $\frac{2}{3}$ of your rectangle. Can you show me a fraction that's *equivalent* to $\frac{2}{3}$? How do you know these fractions are *equivalent*?

SESSION FOLLOW-UP

3 Daily Practice

Daily Practice: For reinforcement of this unit's content, have students complete *Student Activity Book* page 5.

Student Math Handbook: Students and families may use *Student Math Handbook* pages 53–54, 59 for reference and review. See pages 170–176 in the back of this unit.

Fractions of Groups of Things

Math Focus Points

◆ Finding fractional parts of a group (of objects, people, etc.)

◆ Writing, reading, and applying fraction notation

Today's Plan		Materials
① **ACTIVITY** **Fractions of 24**	🕐 20 MIN 👥 CLASS 👤 INDIVIDUALS	• M7 (from Session 1.1); T64 🖥 • Connecting cubes (as needed); chart paper*;colored pencils or crayons
② **ACTIVITY** **Story Problems About 24**	🕐 40 MIN 👤 INDIVIDUALS	• *Student Activity Book,* pp. 6–7 • M7 • Connecting cubes (as needed)
③ **SESSION FOLLOW-UP** **Daily Practice and Homework**		• *Student Activity Book,* p. 8–10 • *Student Math Handbook,* p. 55

*See *Materials to Prepare,* p. 21.

Ten-Minute Math

Practicing Place Value Say "two thousand five hundred sixteen" and have students practice writing the number. Make sure all students can read, write, and say this number correctly. Ask students to solve these problems mentally, if possible:

• What is 2,516 — 10? 2,516 — 30? 2,516 — 300? 2,516 — 500? 2,516 — 1,000?

Write each answer on the board. Ask students to compare each difference with 2,516. Which places have the same digits? Which do not? Why? If time remains, pose additional similar problems using these numbers: 1,730 and 2,191.

Math Note

❶ Fractions of a Group Fractions can represent many kinds of situations. The two that students work with in this unit are fractions of an area and fractions of a group of objects, such as apples or people. As adults, we may no longer see the use of fractions in these two kinds of situations as different. However, for students, dividing a single rectangle into fourths can seem quite different from dividing a group of 24 people into fourths. First, the action is different: to divide a rectangle into fourths, students typically fold or draw lines; to divide a group of 24 people into fourths, students may move counters representing the people into four groups. Second, the arithmetic of dividing a single entity looks different to students than the arithmetic involved in dividing a group. If a rectangle is divided into fourths, each part is $\frac{1}{4}$ of the rectangle ($\frac{1}{4}$ of 1 = $\frac{1}{4}$). If the groups of people are divided in fourths, each of the groups is $\frac{1}{4}$ of the people *and* there are six people in that group ($\frac{1}{4}$ of 24 = 6). It is important that students develop visual images both for parts of one whole and for parts of a group of things, and learn to relate fractions to these parts in both kinds of situations.

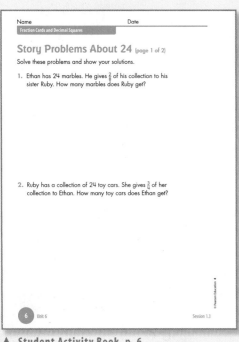

▲ Student Activity Book, p. 6

① ACTIVITY
Fractions of 24

20 MIN CLASS INDIVIDUALS

Students have been using an area model of fractions to think about how a single object, such as a rectangle or a sandwich, can be divided into parts that are named with fractions in relation to that single whole object. In this activity, students focus on finding fractional parts of a group of objects and naming equal parts of the group of things with fractions.❶

We have been finding fractional parts of rectangles by dividing them into equal pieces. So far in this unit, we've been finding fractions of one single thing. It is also possible to find fractional parts of a group of things. Think about this: How many students is $\frac{1}{2}$ of our class?

Show students the problem you wrote on the board or chart paper.

> I have a crate of 24 oranges.
> $\frac{1}{4}$ of the oranges go to Mr. Freed.
> The rest go to Ms. Lee.
>
> What fraction of the oranges will Ms. Lee get?
>
> How many oranges will Mr. Freed get?
>
> How many oranges will Ms. Lee get?

Work with a partner to think about these questions.

Students may use copies of 4 × 6 Rectangles (M7) or connecting cubes to solve this problem.

Bring students together after they have had about five minutes to work on this problem.

How did you solve this problem? Did you use cubes or a drawing to help you?

Students might say:

"I figured out that $\frac{1}{4}$ of the crate is 6 oranges because 4 groups of 6 equals 24. It takes $\frac{4}{4}$ to equal the whole crate, so Ms. Lee gets $\frac{3}{4}$. That's 18 oranges because $6 + 18 = 24$."

"I knew that $\frac{1}{4} + \frac{1}{4} + \frac{1}{4} + \frac{1}{4} = 1$ whole. So if Mr. Freed has $\frac{1}{4}$ and Ms. Lee gets the rest, then Ms. Lee gets $\frac{3}{4}$."

"I used a rectangle to figure it out. I knew that $\frac{1}{4}$ of 24 is 6 because when I find $\frac{1}{4}$ of the 4 × 6 rectangle it has 6 squares. I can divide the rest of the rectangle into 3 more fourths, so Ms. Lee gets $\frac{3}{4}$. That's 18 oranges. I counted up the rest of the squares."

If students do not mention the 4 × 6 rectangle, ask them whether they see how they could use it to represent the crate of 24 oranges. Put up the transparency 4 × 6 Rectangles (T64), showing 24 squares in each rectangle, and ask students to show Mr. Freed's share and Ms. Lee's share on one rectangle. Write $\frac{1}{4}$ and $\frac{3}{4}$ to label each share.

Explain that for the rest of the session, students will be solving some story problems about 24 objects.

* Can use manipulatives

2 sided counters

snap cubes — different colors

▲ Student Activity Book, p. 7

▲ Student Activity Book, p. 8

▲ Student Activity Book, p. 9

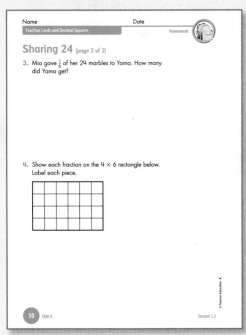

▲ Student Activity Book, p. 10

ACTIVITY

2 Story Problems About 24

40 MIN INDIVIDUALS

Students solve story problems on *Student Activity Book* pages 6–7.

ONGOING ASSESSMENT: Observing Students at Work

Students solve story problems in which they find fractional parts of a group of 24 objects.

- **Can students find fractional parts of 24 objects?**

- **Can students use representations (e.g., rectangles or cubes) to show that they have identified the correct quantity?**

- **Can students find fractional parts of a group of objects represented by fractions with numerators greater than 1?**

SESSION FOLLOW-UP

3 Daily Practice and Homework

 Daily Practice: For ongoing review, have students complete *Student Activity Book* page 8.

 Homework: Students solve word problems on *Student Activity Book* pages 9–10. In these problems, students identify $\frac{1}{2}$, $\frac{1}{3}$, and $\frac{1}{6}$ of a set of marbles.

Student Math Handbook: Students and families may use *Student Math Handbook* page 55 for reference and review. See pages 170–176 in the back of this unit.

Same Parts, Different Wholes

Math Focus Points

◆ Finding fractional parts of a rectangular area

◆ Finding fractional parts of a group (of objects, people, etc.)

◆ Comparing the same fractional parts of different-sized wholes

Today's Plan		Materials
① DISCUSSION **Halves of Different Wholes**	🕐 👥 20 MIN CLASS	• *Student Activity Book*, p. 11 • T66 📠 • Colored pencils or crayons (as needed)
② MATH WORKSHOP **Same Parts, Different Wholes** **②ⓐ Finding Fractions of a 5 x 12 Rectangle** **②ⓑ Story Problems About a Class**	🕐 40 MIN	**②ⓐ** • *Student Activity Book*, p. 11 • M11* • Chart: "Fractions to Find on the 5 × 12 Rectangles"*; colored pencils or crayons (as needed) **②ⓑ** • *Student Activity Book*, pp. 12–13 • M7; M11* • Connecting Cubes (as needed)
③ SESSION FOLLOW-UP **Daily Practice and Homework**		• *Student Activity Book*, pp. 14–15 • *Student Math Handbook*, p. 63 • M13–M14, Family Letter*

*See *Materials to Prepare*, p. 21.

[handwritten: Front load What makes 60]

[handwritten: Differentiate— Do with numerator of 1 first]

Ten-Minute Math

Practicing Place Value Write 4,756 on the board and have students practice saying it. Make sure all students can read, write, and say this number correctly. Ask students to solve these problems mentally, if possible:

• What is 4,756 + 100? 4,756 + 300? 4,756 − 20? 4,756 − 30? 4,756 − 50?

Write each answer on the board. Ask students to compare each sum or difference with 4,756. Which places have the same digits? Which do not? Why? If time remains, pose additional similar problems using these numbers: 3,188 and 7,204.

Math Notes

❶ A Half Is a Half Is a Half This discussion about halves of different wholes is important because it is at the heart of some complicated ideas of fractions. In one sense, $\frac{1}{2}$ is always $\frac{1}{2}$. When represented on a number line, for example, the number $\frac{1}{2}$ always has the same relationship to 1 and to other numbers. However, the quantity represented by $\frac{1}{2}$ depends on the size of the whole quantity—that is, $\frac{1}{2}$ of a class of 22 is 11 students, whereas $\frac{1}{2}$ of a class of 26 is 13 students. Coordinating these two ideas about fractions and what they represent is complex. Students will have time to develop this understanding further as they compare the fractional parts they found of the 4 × 6 rectangle with the same fractional parts of the 5 × 12 rectangle (and later, in Investigation 3, the 10 × 10 rectangle). They work with placing fractions on a number line in Investigation 2.

❷ Measuring Area in Square Units Remind students that the dimensions of these rectangles are 5 centimeters by 12 centimeters and that the area is shown in square centimeters.

❶ Halves of Different Wholes

Math Focus Points for Discussion

◆ Comparing the same fractional parts of different-sized wholes

In this discussion, students compare the same fractional parts of different-sized rectangles.

You have been finding fractional parts of a 4 × 6 rectangle. Now you are going to work with a different rectangle. We are going to think about what is the same and what is different about fractional parts of each of these rectangles.

Display the transparency, 5 × 12 Rectangles (T66) on the overhead projector.

What are the dimensions of this rectangle? [5 × 12] Will $\frac{1}{2}$ of the area of this rectangle be the same size as $\frac{1}{2}$ of the area of the 4 × 6 rectangle?❶

Ask students to use *Student Activity Book* page 11 to show $\frac{1}{2}$ and $\frac{1}{4}$ of the 5 × 12 rectangle in several different ways. Then bring them back together and ask them to compare these fractional parts with the same fractional parts they found on the 4 × 6 rectangle.

What do you notice when you find $\frac{1}{2}$ or $\frac{1}{4}$ of the 5 × 12 rectangle? What is the same and what is different from finding $\frac{1}{2}$ or $\frac{1}{4}$ of the 4 × 6 rectangle?❷

Students might say:

"I found half the same way. I drew a line across the middle and both sides are equal. And I drew a line down the middle the other way and both sides are equal."

"When I divide the 5 × 12 rectangle in half there are 30 squares in each half. There are only 12 in each half of the 4 × 6 rectangle. There are 60 squares in the 5 × 12 rectangle and only 24 in the 4 × 6."

"The halves in the 5 × 12 rectangle are bigger. That is because the whole rectangle is bigger."

Conclude the discussion by asking questions about the same fractional parts of the two sizes of rectangle and the same fractional parts of two different-sized groups of objects or people.

Is $\frac{2}{3}$ of the area of the 5 × 12 rectangle more than $\frac{2}{3}$ of the area of the 4 × 6 rectangle? How do you know?

Is $\frac{1}{2}$ of our class the same size as $\frac{1}{2}$ of the other Grade 4 class? How do you know?

Collect some responses to these questions as time allows.

DIFFERENTIATION: Supporting the Range of Learners

ELL English Language Learners may need practice using comparative vocabulary. Model the terms *greater than, less than, same as,* and *equivalent,* using a "think aloud" strategy as you work with concrete models. Then ask students to practice this vocabulary using the same models. As students work, check for understanding of these terms by asking them to compare fractional parts of rectangles using comparative language and models as necessary.

MATH WORKSHOP

② Same Parts, Different Wholes

40 MIN

Introduce the Math Workshop. Explain that students will be working on two activities that have to do with dividing either a rectangle or a group of things (people or objects) into fractional parts.

In this session, students may choose one of the activities or divide their time between them. They have the chance to work on both activities again when Math Workshop continues in Sessions 1.6 and 1.7.

②A Finding Fractions of a 5 × 12 Rectangle

INDIVIDUALS PAIRS

Students identify and label fractional parts on the 5 × 12 rectangle on *Student Activity Book* page 11, using the list of fractions you have posted on the board or chart paper.

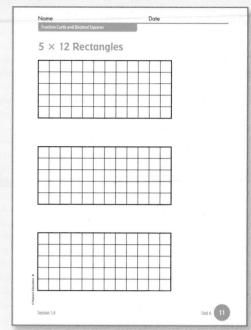

Name _____ Date _____

Fraction Cards and Decimal Squares

5 × 12 Rectangles

Session 1.4   Unit 6 11

▲ **Student Activity Book, p. 11;
Resource Masters, M11; T66**

*first load –
What makes 60 –
factors.*

Fractions to Find on the 5 × 12 Rectangles			
$\frac{1}{4}$	$\frac{1}{3}$	$\frac{1}{12}$	$\frac{5}{6}$
$\frac{2}{3}$	$\frac{1}{6}$	$\frac{2}{4}$	$\frac{3}{6}$
$\frac{1}{5}$	$\frac{4}{12}$	$\frac{3}{5}$	$\frac{2}{5}$
$\frac{6}{12}$	$\frac{4}{6}$	$\frac{4}{5}$	$\frac{3}{4}$

Can put on overhead or Chart paper

When students complete *Student Activity Book* page 11, give them a copy of 5 × 12 Rectangles (M11).

Remind students that the strategies they used to find fractional parts of the 4 × 6 rectangle will be useful for the 5 × 12 rectangle. They might want to think of the factor pairs they know for the area of the rectangle. For example, $3 \times 20 = 60$, so $\frac{1}{3}$ of 60 is 20.

Students might start with the unit fractions ($\frac{1}{2}, \frac{1}{4}, \frac{1}{3}, \frac{1}{6}$) and use these to find other fractions that are related (how can $\frac{1}{6}$ of the area help you find $\frac{1}{12}$ of the area?). They should also be sure to work with some of the fractions with numerators greater than 1, again using fractional parts they have found, such as $\frac{1}{3}$, to find other parts, such as $\frac{2}{3}$.

Keep this list of fractions posted because students will continue working on this activity in Sessions 1.6 and 1.7.

ONGOING ASSESSMENT: Observing Students at Work

Students identify fractional parts of the area of a 5 × 12 rectangle.

- **Can students interpret the meaning of a fraction in the context of area?** For example, do they interpret $\frac{2}{3}$ of the area to mean 2 out of the 3 equal parts that make up the whole?

- **Which of the fractional parts are students able to find easily?** Can they find the most familiar fractional parts, such as $\frac{1}{2}$ and $\frac{1}{4}$? Can they find some of the less familiar fractional parts, such as $\frac{1}{5}$ and $\frac{1}{12}$? Can they find fractional parts represented by fractions with numerators greater than 1, such as $\frac{2}{3}$ and $\frac{3}{5}$?

- **What strategies are students using to find fractional parts of the 5 × 12 rectangle?** Are they counting, making equal shares, or using fractions that they know (e.g., I know how big $\frac{1}{5}$ is and I can double that to find $\frac{2}{5}$)?

- **Do students have any difficulty writing fractional notation?**

As students work, ask questions such as these:

- How do you know that the part you shaded in is $\frac{1}{5}$ of the area of the rectangle? Can you show me $\frac{2}{5}$ of the area? How many square units is that?

- Can you use any of the fractions that have a numerator that is more than 1 to find a part of the area of the rectangle? For example, can you show me $\frac{2}{3}$ of the rectangle?

- How does $\frac{1}{2}$ of this rectangle compare with $\frac{1}{2}$ of the 4 × 6 rectangle? Are they the same size? Which is bigger? Why is that?

DIFFERENTIATION: Supporting the Range of Learners

Intervention If some students have been working more slowly on identifying fractional parts of the 4 × 6 rectangle, allow them to continue working on that rectangle before they move on to the 5 × 12 rectangle. You may want to introduce work on the 5 × 12 rectangle by shading in $\frac{1}{2}$ or $\frac{1}{4}$ and asking them to identify the fractional part. For some students, identifying the part you have shaded is often easier at first than finding the fractional part themselves. After they have worked on a few rectangles that you have shaded, ask them to shade in one of those same parts (such as $\frac{1}{2}$ or $\frac{1}{4}$) in a different way. They can focus at first on fractions that relate to $\frac{1}{2}$ ($\frac{1}{4}$, $\frac{2}{4}$, and $\frac{3}{4}$).

Extension For students who easily show fractional parts represented by the fractions on your list, add fractions that are more challenging. These can include $\frac{1}{10}$, $\frac{3}{10}$, $\frac{7}{10}$, $\frac{8}{10}$, $\frac{1}{15}$, $\frac{3}{15}$, $\frac{5}{15}$, $\frac{9}{15}$, $\frac{1}{30}$, $\frac{10}{30}$, $\frac{15}{30}$, $\frac{20}{30}$, and $\frac{25}{30}$. For extra challenge, students can find $\frac{1}{8}$ or $\frac{5}{8}$ of the rectangle.

Students who are ready for additional challenge can begin working on Combinations That Equal 1, which is introduced in the next session. They use their rectangles to find ways to combine fractions to equal 1.

2B Story Problems About a Class

INDIVIDUALS PAIRS

Students solve word problems in which they find fractional parts of a group of people on *Student Activity Book* pages 12–13. In these problems, students find fractions of different quantities (e.g., 28, 32, 60). Students may use copies of 4 × 6 Rectangles (M7) or 5 × 12 Rectangles (M11) as well as connecting cubes to help them solve these problems.

Remind students to use strategies they used when finding fractional parts of 24. For example, can they find $\frac{1}{2}$ of the quantity? Will that help them find $\frac{1}{4}$ or $\frac{1}{8}$ of the same quantity?

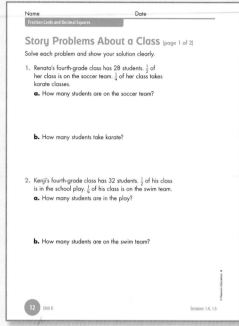

▲ **Student Activity Book, p. 12**

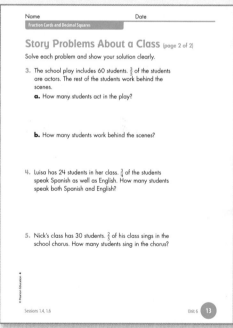

▲ **Student Activity Book, p. 13**

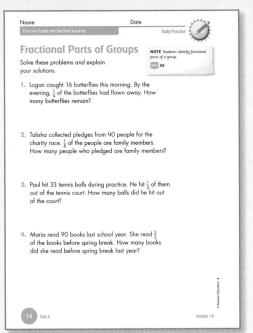

▲ **Student Activity Book, p. 14**

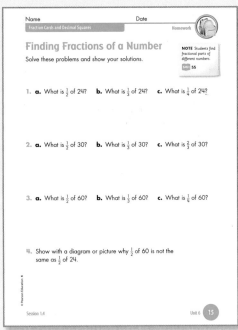

▲ **Student Activity Book, p. 15**

ONGOING ASSESSMENT: Observing Students at Work

Students find fractional parts of a group of people.

- **Can students interpret the meaning of a fraction in the context of groups of people?** For example, do they interpret $\frac{3}{5}$ of a group to mean 3 out of 5 equal parts of the group? (An alternate interpretation is 3 out of every 5 in the group.)

- **Which of the fractional parts are students able to find easily?** Can they find the most familiar fractional parts, such as $\frac{1}{2}$ and $\frac{1}{4}$? Can they find some of the less familiar fractional parts, such as $\frac{1}{5}$ and $\frac{1}{12}$? Can they find fractional parts represented by fractions with numerators greater than 1, such as $\frac{3}{4}$ or $\frac{3}{5}$?

- **Can students use representations to help them solve these problems?**

DIFFERENTIATION: Supporting the Range of Learners

Intervention Help students who are having difficulty visualizing a fractional part of a group to "act out" the problems by using cubes or drawings. Start with unit fractions, such as $\frac{1}{2}$, $\frac{1}{4}$, or $\frac{1}{5}$. For example, for Problem 2, talk through the meaning of $\frac{1}{2}$ of the class and ask students to show you $\frac{1}{2}$ of the class, using cubes or Xs on paper. Then ask students to explain the meaning of $\frac{1}{4}$ of the class and again act it out. Repeat this with one of the less familiar fractions, such as $\frac{1}{5}$.

SESSION FOLLOW-UP

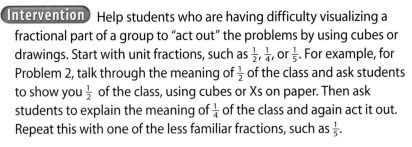

3 Daily Practice and Homework

Daily Practice: For reinforcement of this unit's content, have students complete *Student Activity Book* page 14.

Homework: Students complete *Student Activity Book* page 15. They find fractional parts of 24, 30, and 60.

Student Math Handbook: Students and families may use *Student Math Handbook* page 63 for reference and review. See pages 170–176 in the back of this unit.

Family Letter: Send home copies of the Family Letter (M13–M14) to provide families with more information about this unit.

Assessment: Identifying and Comparing Fractions

Math Focus Points

◆ Finding fractional parts of a rectangular area

◆ Writing, reading, and applying fraction notation

◆ Using representations to add fractions that sum to 1

Today's Plan		Materials
ACTIVITY **①** **Combinations That Equal 1**	30 MIN CLASS INDIVIDUALS	• T66 ; M11 • Chart: "Combinations of Fractions that Equal 1"*; colored pencils or crayons (as needed)
ASSESSMENT ACTIVITY **②** **Identifying and Comparing Fractions**	✓ 30 MIN INDIVIDUALS	• M12*
SESSION FOLLOW-UP **③** **Daily Practice and Homework**		• *Student Activity Book*, pp. 17–18 • *Student Math Handbook*, pp. 54–57

*See *Materials to Prepare*, p. 21.

Ten-Minute Math

Practicing Place Value Say "one thousand fifty" and have students practice writing the number. Make sure all students can read, write, and say this number correctly. Ask students to solve these problems mentally, if possible:

- What is $1{,}050 + 50$? $1{,}050 + 1000$? $1{,}050 - 50$? $1{,}050 - 100$? $1{,}050 - 1000$?

Write each answer on the board. Ask students to compare each sum or difference with 1,050. Which places have the same digits? Which do not? Why? If time remains, pose additional similar problems using these numbers: 6,946 and 2,840.

Need to know the
whole before you can
decide

- 2 different size pizzas

- oranges in crate like Mr Fred
  his or this

- Area model-
  to build house as
  bigger area

ACTIVITY

30 MIN CLASS INDIVIDUALS

① Combinations That Equal 1

In this activity, students focus on sums of fractional parts that equal 1. They divide a 5 × 12 rectangle into different fractional parts and label each part. Then they record what they have done as an equation (e.g., $\frac{1}{2} + \frac{1}{4} + \frac{1}{4} = 1$). Introduce this activity by displaying the transparency 5 × 12 Rectangles (T66) and draw a line that marks $\frac{1}{4}$ of the rectangle. Students should also have a copy of 5 × 12 Rectangles (M11) to work on.

M 11

We have been finding different fractions on these 5 × 12 rectangles and labeling each one. Now, I want you to find ways to divide this whole rectangle into different fractions so that each piece is labeled and all together they equal the whole rectangle.

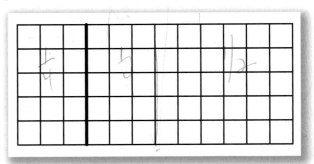

This is $\frac{1}{4}$ of the whole rectangle. [Point to the section of the rectangle on the transparency.] If I want to divide this rectangle into a total of three or four pieces, can you come up with one or two ways that I can divide it? Start with the $\frac{1}{4}$ section like the one here, and then find at least one way to divide up the rest. You have been finding many different fractional parts of this 5 by 12 rectangle, so you have many different possibilities. Label your parts and write an equation that shows how your parts add up to the whole rectangle. For example, if you divided the rest of this rectangle into one more fourth and one half, what equation would you write?

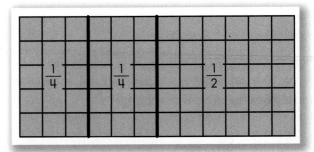

Allow students a few minutes to work on this task. Encourage them to share their work with a partner and check each other's work.

Collect a few examples to share on the overhead. As students share, record on the chart, "Combinations of Fractions That Equal 1," an equation for each rectangle that shows how the fractional parts add up to 1.

Combinations of Fractions That Equal 1

$$\frac{1}{4} + \frac{1}{4} + \frac{1}{2} = 1$$

$$\frac{1}{3} + \frac{1}{6} + \frac{2}{4} = 1$$

$$\frac{1}{4} + \frac{5}{12} + \frac{1}{3} = 1$$

Choose one example that you think will challenge the class, either from a student example or one you pose.

As you were working, I noticed someone had an equation that read: $\frac{1}{4} + \frac{1}{2} + \frac{1}{6} + \frac{1}{12} = 1$. Is that true? How could you know for sure?

Allow students a few minutes to work on this, and then collect some responses. Encourage students to show their reasoning on the rectangles or with cubes.

If time allows, students can work on finding more ways to combine fractions to equal 1. Let students know that they will have time to work on this activity over the next two days in Math Workshop and that they can add any new combinations they find to the chart.

Keep this chart, along with the "Fractions That Are Equal" chart, posted until the end of the unit. Remind students to add to them. ❶

ONGOING ASSESSMENT: Observing Students at Work

Students find different ways to divide a 5 × 12 rectangle into fractional parts.

- **Can students divide a rectangle into fractional parts and identify each of the fractions that they draw?**

- **Can they write an equation that represents the sum of all the fractional parts equaling 1?**

Teaching Note

❶ **Same or Different?** Students will encounter mathematical activities in which a different arrangement of the same mathematical objects—shapes or numbers, for example—are considered the same or different, depending on the mathematical purpose. For example, 6 × 3 is the same as 3 × 6 in that both have the same product. However, if these expressions represent different situations, 6 bags with 3 marbles in each bag is different from 3 bags with 6 marbles in each bag. In this activity, students are looking for different *combinations* of fractional parts that make a whole, without regard for their order or arrangement. Let students know that for this activity, you want them to consider two combinations made with the same fractions to be the same solution, even though in some other context, it could be important to find all the different arrangements.

rolling cubes

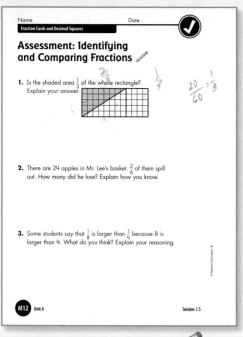

▲ **Resource Masters, M12** PORTFOLIO WRITING

Intervention This can be a challenging activity for students who are not yet comfortable identifying a wide variety of fractions. Encourage students to start with fractions that are most familiar to them (e.g., $\frac{1}{2} + \frac{1}{4} + \frac{1}{4}$). If students seem stuck, provide a starter. For example, label $\frac{1}{2}$ of the rectangle as one fractional part, and see whether the student can divide up the rest of the rectangle.

Extension For students who are easily finding and labeling some of the most familiar fractions, such as halves, fourths, and thirds, provide a challenging starter. For example, mark off (but do not label) $\frac{5}{12}$ of the rectangle or $\frac{1}{10}$ of the rectangle, and ask students to complete dividing up and labeling the parts.

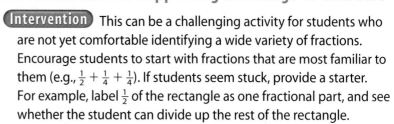

ASSESSMENT ACTIVITY

30 MIN INDIVIDUALS

2 Identifying and Comparing Fractions

Students work on Assessment: Identifying and Comparing Fractions (M12) to assess their understanding of four of the benchmarks for this unit: Benchmark 1: Identify fractional parts of an area; Benchmark 2: Identify fractional parts of a group (of objects, people, etc.); Benchmark 3: Read, write, and interpret fraction notation; and Benchmark 4: Order fractions with like and unlike denominators.

In these problems, students show whether they can identify a fractional part of a rectangle and a fractional part of a group of things. They show their understanding of one of the building blocks of ordering fractions when they justify whether $\frac{1}{4}$ is more or less than $\frac{1}{8}$. They also show how well they understand the meaning of the written notation for fractions throughout their responses.

Students should work on this assessment individually.

*Students demonstrate their ability to identify
fractional parts of an area.*

 SESSION FOLLOW-UP

3 Daily Practice and Homework

 Daily Practice: For ongoing review, have students complete
Student Activity Book page 17.

Homework: On *Student Activity Book* page 18, students shade
in approximate fractional parts of un-gridded rectangles. They
explain their reasoning about how much of the rectangle to
shade in.

Student Math Handbook: Students and families may use
Student Math Handbook pages 54–57 for reference and
review. See pages 170–176 in the back of this unit.

Professional Development

❷ **Teacher Note:** Assessment: Identifying and
Comparing Fractions, p. 143

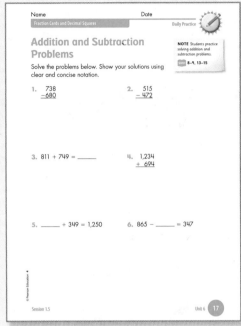

▲ **Student Activity Book, p. 17**

▲ **Student Activity Book, p. 18**

Combinations That Equal 1

Math Focus Points

◆ Using representations to add fractions that sum to 1

◆ Adding fractions with the same and related denominators
(e.g., halves, fourths, and eighths; thirds and sixths)

Today's Plan		Materials
ACTIVITY **❶ Introduction to Adding Fractions**	🕐 **20 MIN** 👥 **CLASS**	• T64 🖨; T66 🖨
MATH WORKSHOP **❷ Fractions** 　**❷Ⓐ Adding Fractions** 　**❷Ⓑ Combinations That Equal 1** 　**❷Ⓒ Finding Fractions of a Rectangle** 　**(5 × 12 and 10 × 10)** 　**❷Ⓓ Story Problems About a Class**	🕐 **40 MIN**	**Ⓐ** • *Student Activity Book,* pp. 19–21 • M7; M11 • Counters (as needed) **Ⓑ** • *Student Activity Book,* p. 22 • Chart: "Combinations of Fractions That Equal 1" (from Session 1.5); colored pencils or crayons **Ⓒ** • *Student Activity Book,* p. 23 • M11; M15* • Chart: "Fractions to Find on the 10 × 10 Squares"* (optional); colored pencils or crayons **Ⓓ** • *Student Activity Book,* pp. 12–13 • M7; M11 • Connecting cubes (as needed)
SESSION FOLLOW-UP **❸ Daily Practice**		• *Student Activity Book,* p. 24 • *Student Math Handbook,* p. 62

*See *Materials to Prepare,* p. 23.

Ten-Minute Math

Practicing Place Value Write 4,307 on the board and have students practice saying it. Make sure that all students can read, write, and say this number correctly. Ask students to solve these problems mentally, if possible:

• What is 4,307 − 300? 4,307 − 400? 4,307 + 30? 4,307 + 50?

Ask students to compare each sum and difference with 4,307. Which places have the same digits? Which do not? Why? If time remains, pose additional similar problems with the numbers 5,375 and 7,211.

ACTIVITY

Introduction to Adding Fractions

20 MIN   CLASS

Students are introduced to using what they know about representing fractions and about fraction equivalencies to add familiar fractions.

Write the following equation on the board:

$$\frac{1}{2} + \frac{2}{6} = \frac{5}{6}$$

Is this equation true? Show how you know.

Allow students to work on this problem for a few minutes. Encourage students to use a rectangle, drawings of objects, or cubes to represent the equation. Also encourage students to estimate whether $\frac{5}{6}$ is a reasonable sum for $\frac{1}{2}$ and $\frac{2}{6}$.

Ask students to share their ideas. Students' explanations should draw on their work with fractional parts of rectangles and their knowledge of equivalencies.

Students might say:

 "I know that $\frac{2}{6} = \frac{1}{3}$. So I am adding $\frac{1}{2}$ and $\frac{1}{3}$. I had to draw it on a rectangle to make sure. Here is $\frac{1}{2}$ plus $\frac{1}{3}$. Each row down is $\frac{1}{6}$ and there are $\frac{5}{6}$. So it is true."

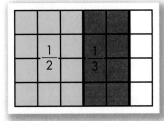

 "If we were adding $\frac{1}{2}$ and $\frac{1}{2}$ it would be 1 whole, so a little less than 1 whole seems right."

"$\frac{1}{2}$ is the same as $\frac{3}{6}$, so then it's easy to add: $\frac{3}{6}$ and $\frac{2}{6}$ is $\frac{5}{6}$."

Math Note

❷ **Adding Fractions** As students develop their understanding of addition with fractions, it is important that they continue to use representations such as their own pictures or rectangles. It is also important that they base their reasoning on combinations of fractions and equivalent fractions that they already know. As they use and represent what they know about fractions, they develop the conceptual understanding that is the basis for the techniques and algorithms for adding fractions that they will encounter in middle school. For example, when students use the idea that $\frac{1}{2} = \frac{3}{6}$ to find the sum of $\frac{1}{2} + \frac{2}{6}$, they are developing ideas about how common denominators are useful for computation with fractions. The focus in this unit is on developing this conceptual understanding about fraction relationships. Although students add fractions and decimal fractions in this unit, addition of fractions and decimals is not a benchmark in Grade 4. Fourth graders are still developing a deep and solid understanding of these numbers. Adding fractions and decimal fractions is a focus of two units in Grade 5, *What's That Portion?* and *Decimals on Grids and Number Lines.*

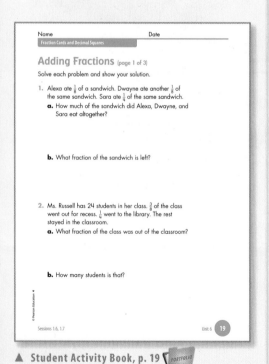

▲ **Student Activity Book, p. 19**

Now write the following on the board and ask students to think about the sum:

$$\frac{1}{2} + \frac{2}{6} + \frac{1}{2} =$$

What if we add another $\frac{1}{2}$? Now what is the sum?

Some students may add on $\frac{1}{2}$ to the previous sum. Others may notice that they can add $\frac{1}{2} + \frac{1}{2}$ to get 1 and then easily add on $\frac{2}{6}$ to get a sum of $1\frac{2}{6}$ (or $1\frac{1}{3}$).

Collect a few examples of how students added these fractions and model them on the transparencies 4 × 6 Rectangles (T64) or 5 × 12 Rectangles (T66), as well as with a set of objects.

How can you show $\frac{1}{2} + \frac{2}{6} + \frac{1}{2}$ on these 4 × 6 rectangles? What if we thought about boxes like those you see in the supermarket with 24 apples in each box? What would $\frac{1}{2} + \frac{2}{6} + \frac{1}{2}$ of boxes of apples look like?

Explain that they will be working on problems that involve adding fractions in the following Math Workshop.❷

MATH WORKSHOP

② Fractions

40 MIN

Students work on several activities in Sessions 1.6 and 1.7 that involve finding fractional parts of an area or of a group of things and adding fractions. In the activity Finding Fractions of a Rectangle, students work with the 5 × 12 Rectangles and are introduced to 10 × 10 Squares.

②A Adding Fractions

INDIVIDUALS

Students solve problems on *Student Activity Book* pages 19–21, in which they add fractions with like and unlike denominators. Students can show their reasoning by using representations and/or by calling on their knowledge of equivalent fractions and fraction combinations.

It is also important to make sure that students do not begin to make common errors in adding fractions, especially when the problems are presented as numbers without a context. Some students, especially less confident students, may try to apply some kind of procedure based on what they know about whole numbers when they see problems with fractions. For example, watch for students who add numerators and denominators (e.g., incorrectly calculating $\frac{1}{2} + \frac{3}{8} = \frac{4}{10}$). Remind them to use what they know about fractions and have them use representations to show how the fractions relate to a whole.

ONGOING ASSESSMENT: Observing Students at Work

Students add fractions by using what they know about representing fractions and reasoning from their knowledge of equivalent fractions and fraction combinations.

- **Do students understand the meaning of fractions in the context of the area of a rectangle?** In the context of a group of things? When presented without a context?

- **What representations are students using to add fractions? Are they using a rectangle? A group of objects?** Can they show the value of unit fractions as well as fractions with a numerator greater than 1 (e.g., $\frac{3}{2}$)? When problems are presented without a context, can students use representations or story contexts to help visualize the fractions and their relationships?

- **Are students using knowledge of equivalent fractions and fraction combinations to solve the problems?** Which equivalent fractions can they use to solve other problems? Which combinations of fractions can they use?

- **Can students add fractions with like denominators (e.g., $\frac{1}{3} + \frac{2}{3}$) mentally and explain how they know what the sum is?** Are students developing and using a repertoire of familiar fraction combinations they "just know" (e.g., $\frac{1}{2} + \frac{1}{4} = \frac{3}{4}, \frac{1}{3} + \frac{1}{6} = \frac{1}{2}$)?

- **Can students solve problems with sums greater than 1?** Do they know how to write a mixed number?

2B Combinations That Equal 1

INDIVIDUALS

Students find different combinations of fractional parts of a 4×6 rectangle that equal the whole rectangle on *Student Activity Book* page 22. They draw and label each fraction on the rectangle and write an equation to represent the sum of all the parts; for example, $\frac{1}{2} + \frac{1}{6} + \frac{1}{3} = 1$, or $\frac{3}{8} + \frac{3}{8} + \frac{1}{4} = 1$. Encourage students to include some fractions with numerators greater than 1.

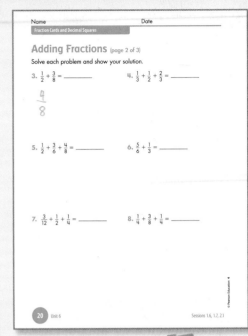

▲ **Student Activity Book, p. 20**

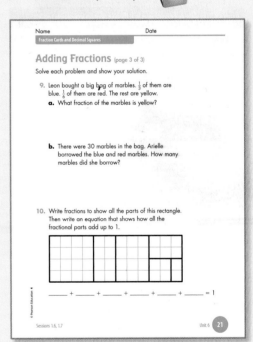

▲ **Student Activity Book, p. 21**

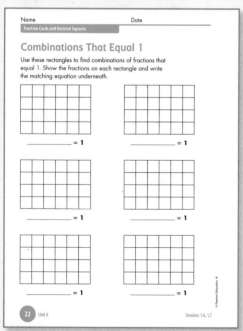

▲ **Student Activity Book, p. 22**

As students work, ask them to add new combinations that equal 1 to the class chart. ❸ ❹

ONGOING ASSESSMENT: Observing Students at Work

Students find different ways to divide a 4 × 6 rectangle into fractional parts.

- **Can students divide the rectangle into parts and correctly label each of the fractional parts?**

- **Which fractions can students use easily?** Can they use thirds and twelfths as well as the more familiar halves, fourths, and eighths? Can they correctly identify fractional parts with numerators greater than 1 as well as unit fractions?

- **Can they write an equation that represents the sum of the fractional parts?**

DIFFERENTIATION: Supporting the Range of Learners

Intervention If a student seems stuck, provide a starter; for example, label $\frac{1}{2}$ of the rectangle as one fractional part, and see whether the student can divide up the rest of the rectangle.

Extension For students who are easily finding and labeling some of the most familiar fractions, such as halves, fourths, and thirds, provide a challenging starter. For example, mark off (but do not label) $\frac{5}{12}$ of the rectangle or $\frac{3}{8}$ of the rectangle, and ask students to complete dividing up and labeling the parts.

2C Finding Fractions of a Rectangle (5 × 12 and 10 × 10)

INDIVIDUALS PAIRS

For complete details about this activity, see Session 1.4, pages 43–44. Students can continue to find fractions of the 5 × 12 Rectangle (M11) and then work with 10 × 10 Squares on *Student Activity Book* page 23. If students complete *Student Activity Book* page 23, give them a copy of 10 × 10 Squares (M15).

Finding fractions of the 10 × 10 square provides the opportunity to continue to reinforce the idea that the same fractional parts of different wholes are different sizes (i.e., $\frac{1}{4}$ of the 10 × 10 square is a different size from $\frac{1}{4}$ of the 4 × 6 rectangle).

Students can refer to the list of fractions you already posted for work on the 5×12 rectangle. You can post a list for the 10×10 square or leave the work more open-ended. Ask students:

What fractions of the 10×10 square can you find easily? Can you challenge yourself to find some more difficult fractions?

If you decide to post a list to get students started, you can use the following fractions:

Fractions to Find on the 10×10 Squares			
$\frac{1}{10}$	$\frac{2}{10}$	$\frac{1}{4}$	$\frac{1}{5}$
$\frac{2}{4}$	$\frac{3}{10}$	$\frac{2}{5}$	$\frac{3}{4}$
$\frac{4}{5}$	$\frac{5}{10}$	$\frac{1}{20}$	$\frac{10}{20}$

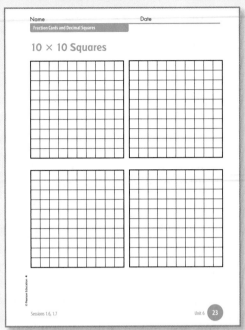

▲ Student Activity Book, p. 23;
Resource Masters, M15; T67

DIFFERENTIATION: Supporting the Range of Learners

Extension Challenge students who can easily identify halves, fourths, fifths, tenths, and twentieths on the 10×10 square to find some fractions that require thinking about parts of squares, such as $\frac{1}{8}$. If students seem stuck, suggest that they first think about $\frac{4}{8}$ and $\frac{2}{8}$. Students can also work to find $\frac{1}{3}$ of the 10×10 square.

2D Story Problems About a Class

INDIVIDUALS   PAIRS

For complete details about this activity, see Session 1.4, page 45.

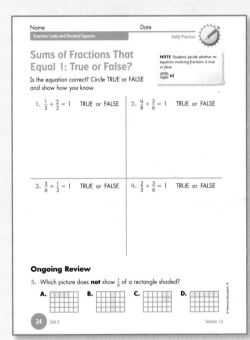

▲ Student Activity Book, p. 24

SESSION FOLLOW-UP
3 Daily Practice

 Daily Practice: For reinforcement of this unit's content, have students complete *Student Activity Book* page 24.

Student Math Handbook: Students and families may use *Student Math Handbook* page 62 for reference and review. See pages 170–176 in the back of this unit.

Adding Fractions

Math Focus Points

◆ Estimating sums of fractions

◆ Using representations to add fractions that sum to 1

◆ Adding fractions with the same and related denominators
   (e.g., halves, fourths, and eighths; thirds and sixths)

Today's Plan		Materials
① DISCUSSION **More or Less Than 1?** 🕐 15 MIN 👥 CLASS 🧍 INDIVIDUALS		• M7 (as needed)
② MATH WORKSHOP **Fractions** **②A Adding Fractions** **②B Combinations That Equal 1** **②C Finding Fractions of a Rectangle** **(5 × 12 and 10 × 10)** 🕐 45 MIN		**②A** • *Student Activity Book,* pp. 19–21 • M7; M11 (as needed) • Counters (as needed) **②B** • *Student Activity Book,* p. 22 • Chart: "Combinations of Fractions That Equal 1" (from Session 1.5) **②C** • *Student Activity Book,* p. 23 • M11; M15 (as needed) • Chart: "Fractions to Find on the 10 × 10 Squares" (optional); colored pencils or crayons
③ SESSION FOLLOW-UP **Daily Practice**		• *Student Activity Book,* p. 25 • *Student Math Handbook,* p. 62

Ten-Minute Math

Practicing Place Value Say "one thousand five" and have students practice writing
the number. Ask students to solve these problems mentally, if possible:

• What is $1{,}005 + 50$? $1{,}005 + 60$? $1{,}005 + 80$? $1{,}005 + 200$? $1{,}005 + 400$?

Ask students to compare each sum with 1,005. If time remains, pose additional
similar problems with the numbers 8,928 and 4,042.

DISCUSSION

1 More or Less Than 1?

15 MIN   CLASS   INDIVIDUALS

Math Focus Points for Discussion

◆ Estimating sums of fractions

As students use representations of fractions and solve problems of fractions in contexts, they internalize mental images of fractions and their relationships. This activity encourages students to use such mental images of fractions to visualize how fractions are related to one another and to 1.

Write on the board or overhead $\frac{1}{2} + \frac{3}{4}$.

Is the sum of $\frac{1}{2}$ and $\frac{3}{4}$ more or less than 1? You don't have to figure out the exact answer. Can you picture these fractions? What do you know about them?

Some students may quickly solve the problem mentally. Others may determine whether the sum is more or less than 1 by estimating. Students should share their thinking with a partner before you collect ideas from the whole class.

Collect a few examples of how students determined their answers. Listen for student ideas that focus on combinations that they know equal 1 and on comparing fractions that are more or less than other fractions. Encourage students to create a picture in their mind to help them and ask them to share their visual images.

Students might say:

"$\frac{1}{2}$ plus $\frac{1}{2}$ equals 1 whole, but $\frac{3}{4}$ is more than $\frac{1}{2}$, so the total has to be more than 1."

"If you have $\frac{3}{4}$ of a pizza, there's only one more $\frac{1}{4}$, but you're adding $\frac{1}{2}$, so it's going to be more than one whole."

"You can split up $\frac{1}{2}$ into two fourths. So one of those fourths goes with $\frac{3}{4}$ to make 1, then you still have an extra fourth. I was picturing it like in a rectangle. You'd have $\frac{3}{4}$ and one of the fourths to make a whole rectangle. Then you'd have a fourth of another rectangle."

Continue the discussion with two more expressions: $\frac{4}{8} + \frac{2}{8}$ and $\frac{5}{6} + \frac{7}{8}$. Write each expression on the board or overhead.

Give students a minute to think about whether each sum is more or less than 1 and jot down their thinking in some way.

Many students will recognize that the fractions in the first expression, $\frac{4}{8} + \frac{2}{8}$, are equivalent to $\frac{1}{2}$ and $\frac{1}{4}$, respectively. They may also argue that 4 of the 8 parts plus 2 of the 8 parts will not equal one whole, which would be 8 of 8 parts.

The second expression, $\frac{5}{6} + \frac{7}{8}$, is more challenging. Students may notice that both $\frac{5}{6}$ and $\frac{7}{8}$ are one small piece ($\frac{1}{6}$ and $\frac{1}{8}$, respectively) less than 1 whole, so together they must be more than 1. You may want to extend the discussion about this problem to include this question:

Do you think the sum of $\frac{5}{6} + \frac{7}{8}$ will be closer to 1 or 2?

It is not expected that students find the exact answer to this problem, but some students may enjoy the challenge of working on this problem by using the 4×6 rectangles (M7). They may be able to solve the problem by using the representations and asking for help in naming the mixed number.

MATH WORKSHOP

45 MIN

2 Fractions

Students continue to work on the Math Workshop activities they began in Session 1.6. Make sure that most students solve all of the problems in Activity 2A, Adding Fractions. Students who are having difficulty identifying a range of fractional parts of a rectangular area should continue to work on Activity 2C, Finding Fractions of a Rectangle. This activity can be very engaging for many students, but those who do not need more practice should spend more time on Combinations That Equal 1 and Adding Fractions.

Remind students to continue to add new combinations of fractions that equal 1 to the class chart.

2A Adding Fractions

INDIVIDUALS

Remind students to look at each problem and think about what a reasonable sum should be before solving the problems, just as they would with whole numbers.

Is it more or less than 1? Close to $\frac{1}{2}$? Close to 1? Close to 2?

For complete details about this activity, see Session 1.6, pages 54–55.

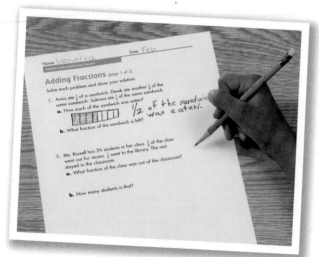

Students use representations and their knowledge of equivalent fractions and fraction combinations to add fractions.

2B Combinations That Equal 1

INDIVIDUALS

For complete details about this activity, see Session 1.6, page 55.

2C Finding Fractions of a Rectangle (5 × 12 and 10 × 10)

INDIVIDUALS PAIRS

For complete details about this activity, see Sessions 1.4, pages 43–44, and 1.6, pages 56–57. When students complete *Student Activity Book* page 23, give them a copy of 10 × 10 Squares (M15).

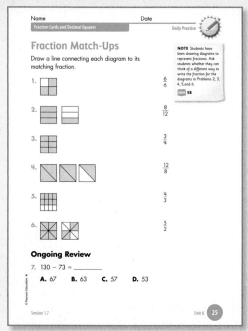

SESSION FOLLOW-UP

3 Daily Practice

Daily Practice: For reinforcement of today's session, have students complete *Student Activity Book* page 25.

Student Math Handbook: Students and families may use *Student Math Handbook* page 62 for reference and review. See pages 170–176 in the back of this unit.

Mathematical Emphases

Rational Numbers Understanding the meaning of fractions and decimal fractions

Math Focus Points

- Finding fractional parts of a rectangular area

- Interpreting the meaning of the numerator and the denominator of a fraction

- Representing fractions greater than 1

Rational Numbers Comparing the values of fractions and decimal fractions

Math Focus Points

- Ordering fractions and justifying their order through reasoning about fraction equivalencies and relationships

- Identifying equivalent fractions

- Comparing fractions to the landmarks 0, $\frac{1}{2}$, 1, and 2

- Representing fractions using a number line

Ordering Fractions

SESSION 2.1 p. 68	Student Activity Book	Student Math Handbook	Professional Development: Read Ahead of Time	
Fraction Cards Students discuss how to represent and notate fractions greater than 1. They begin making a set of Fraction Cards that show area representations for a variety of fractions, including fractions with numerators greater than the denominators, and mixed numbers.	20, 26–29	53, 58	• **Part 4: Ten-Minute Math** in *Implementing Investigations in Grade 4:* Quick Survey • **Teacher Note:** Keeping Track of the Whole, p. 149	
SESSION 2.2 p. 74				
Fraction Cards, *continued* Students complete their set of Fraction Cards. They develop arguments about the relative size of two fractions, $\frac{1}{2}$ and $\frac{5}{6}$, that are each one fractional part less than a whole.	26–27, 31–32	56–57		
SESSION 2.3 p. 78				
Capture Fractions Students compare pairs of fractions, using what they know about fraction equivalencies and relationships of fractions to $\frac{1}{2}$ and 1, in a class discussion and in the game *Capture Fractions*.	33–35	59–61; G1	• **Teacher Note:** Visualizing Fraction Equivalencies, p. 141 • **Teacher Note:** Strategies for Comparing Fractions, p. 151	

Materials to Gather	Materials to Prepare
• **M19, How to Make Fraction Cards** (as needed) • **Colored pencils or crayons** (as needed) • **Scissors** (1 per pair) • **Glue sticks** (1 per pair) • **Rulers** (optional)	• **M7, 4 × 6 Rectangles** Make copies. (1 per student) • **M16, Blank Wholes for Fraction Cards** Make copies. (1 per student, plus extras) • **M17, Blank Thirds for Fraction Cards** Make copies. (1 per student, plus extras) • **M18, Blank Fifths for Fraction Cards** Make copies. (1 per student, plus extras) • **Fraction Cards** Each group of 3–4 students will make one deck of Fraction Cards. For each deck cut 10 pieces of colored oak tag or card stock, $8\frac{1}{2}''$ x 11″, in fourths to make 40 cards that are $4\frac{1}{4}''$ x $5\frac{1}{2}''$. If possible, use different colors of oak tag for each deck. • $\frac{3}{5}$ **and** $1\frac{1}{2}$ **Fraction Cards** Use the Blank Wholes for Fraction Cards (M16) to make two sample Fraction Cards for $\frac{3}{5}$ and $1\frac{1}{2}$. Draw a representation of each fraction, cut out and glue onto two blank Fraction Cards. See the illustration, p. 71 and the directions on How to Make Fraction Cards (M19).
• **M16, Blank Wholes for Fraction Cards** (from Session 2.1; as needed) • **M17, Blank Thirds for Fraction Cards** (from Session 2.1; as needed) • **M18, Blank Fifths for Fraction Cards** (from Session 2.1; as needed) • **Colored oak tag or card stock** (cut in fourths, from Session 2.1) • **Scissors** (1 per pair) • **Glue sticks** (1 per pair) • **Rulers** (optional) • **Colored pencils or crayons** (as needed)	
• **Connecting cubes** (as needed)	• **M20, *Capture Fractions*** Review the directions for *Capture Fractions*. Make copies. (as needed) • **M21, Finding Equivalent Fractions** Make copies. (as needed) • **Chart paper** Draw a picture of $\frac{1}{4}$ and $\frac{3}{5}$ Fraction Cards on one piece of chart paper and a picture of $\frac{2}{3}$ and $\frac{5}{6}$ Fraction Cards on another. See illustration, pp. 79–80.

Ordering Fractions, *continued*

SESSION 2.4 p. 83	Student Activity Book	Student Math Handbook	Professional Development: Read Ahead of Time	
Comparing Fractions to Landmarks Students compare fractions to the landmarks 0, $\frac{1}{2}$, 1, and 2.	37–38	60–61	• **Dialogue Box:** Comparing Fractions to Landmarks, p. 165	
SESSION 2.5 p. 88				
Fractions on a Number Line Students compare pairs of fractions to determine which is larger. They order fractions on a number line by identifying equivalent fractions and making comparisons to landmarks such as $\frac{1}{2}$ and 1.	39–41	60–61; G1		
SESSION 2.6 p. 94				
Assessment: Comparing Fractions Students continue to order fractions on a number line. They are assessed on comparing pairs of fractions. They discuss strategies and their conjectures about general rules for fraction comparisons.	39, 43	60–61; G1	• **Teacher Note:** Assessment: Comparing Fractions, p. 153 • **Dialogue Box:** Conjectures About Fractions, p. 167	

Materials to Gather	Materials to Prepare
• **T68, Table for Grouping Fractions Between Landmarks** • **Fraction Cards** (from Session 2.3; 1 per group)	• **Landmark Cards** Prepare a set of Landmark Cards for each group of 4 students. For each set, cut one piece of oak tag in fourths to make 4 cards that are $4\frac{1}{4}$" x $5\frac{1}{2}$". Write each of the numbers 0, $\frac{1}{2}$, 1, and 2 on one card. Make an extra set for use in the next session. • **Chart paper** Title a sheet of chart paper "Conjectures About Fractions."
• **M20, *Capture Fractions*** (from Session 2.3) • **M21, Finding Equivalent Fractions** (from Session 2.3; as needed) • $\frac{3}{8}$ **and** $\frac{2}{4}$ **Fraction Cards** (Pull these from the class deck.) • **Class deck of Fraction Cards** (from Session 2.1) • **Clothesline** (about 9 feet; optional) • **Paper clips** (optional) • **Adding machine tape** (optional) • **Fraction Cards** (from Session 2.3; 1 deck per group) • **Chart: "Conjectures About Fractions"** (from Session 2.4) • **Connecting cubes** (as needed)	• **Class Fraction Number Line** Set up a fraction number line in a place students can both reach and see when they gather as a whole group. To accommodate a full set of cards, you will need a space about 9 feet long. The number line itself may be either a sturdy clothesline, on which students will hang the cards with paper clips, or a strip of paper (perhaps adding machine tape) taped to a board or wall with space beneath for students to tape their cards. You will also need a set of Landmark Cards like the ones students used in Session 2.4. These should be placed approximately where they would fall on the number line but should not be permanently fixed because students may need to slide them along the number line to fit more cards between. If you are using a clothesline, punch a hole in the top and bottom of each card in the class deck. Students then thread paper clips through the holes in order to hang the cards from the number line and from one another (for equivalent fractions). See illustration, p. 90. • **Space for student work** Decide how to handle the space needs for pairs of students working on their fraction number lines. See Session 2.5 for more detail. • **Adding machine tape** Cut in 6-foot lengths. (1 per group of 4, optional)
• **M20, *Capture Fractions*** (from Session 2.3) • **M21, Finding Equivalent Fractions** (from Session 2.3; as needed) • **Class Fraction Number Line** (from Session 2.5) • **Class deck of Fraction Cards** (from Session 2.1) • **Fraction Cards** (from Session 2.3; 1 deck per group) • **Adding machine tape** (optional) • **Connecting cubes** (as needed) • **Chart: "Conjectures About Fractions"** (from Session 2.4) • **Chart paper** (optional)	• **M23, Assessment: Comparing Fractions** Make copies. (1 per student)

 Overhead Transparency

Fraction Cards

Math Focus Points

- Interpreting the meaning of the numerator and the denominator of a fraction
- Representing fractions greater than 1
- Finding fractional parts of a rectangular area

Today's Plan		Materials
DISCUSSION ❶ **Fractions Greater Than 1**	🕐 20 MIN 👥 CLASS	• *Student Activity Book*, p. 20 • M7* • Colored pencils or crayons (as needed)
ACTIVITY ❷ **Making Fraction Cards**	🕐 40 MIN 👥 GROUPS	• *Student Activity Book*, pp. 26–27 • M16*; M17*; M18*; M19 • $\frac{3}{5}$ and $1\frac{1}{2}$ Fraction Cards*; colored oak tag or card stock; scissors; glue sticks; rulers; colored pencils or crayons
SESSION FOLLOW-UP ❸ **Daily Practice and Homework**		• *Student Activity Book*, pp. 28–29 • *Student Math Handbook*, pp. 53, 58

*See *Materials to Prepare,* p. 65.

Ten-Minute Math

Quick Survey For the survey, ask the class how many books they have read in the past 30 days or a different numerical question that you or students choose. Make sure that they collect data about something they already know or can observe easily. With today's data, make a line plot.

- What do you notice about the data? What do the data tell us about our class?

20 MIN **CLASS**

① Fractions Greater Than 1

Math Focus Points for Discussion

◆ Interpreting the meaning of the numerator and the denominator of a fraction

◆ Representing fractions greater than 1

This Investigation focuses on comparing and ordering fractions, including fractions greater than 1. Start by asking students to look at Problems 3 through 6 on *Student Activity Book* page 20, which they completed in Session 1.7.

Which of these addition problems has a sum that is greater than one? Which ones have a sum less than 1? Could you tell which ones have sums less or more than 1 even before you figured out the exact answers?

After hearing some of your students' ideas, focus on Problem 5.

$$\frac{1}{2} + \frac{3}{6} + \frac{4}{8} =$$

Ask students how they solved this problem and how they expressed their answers. If some students wrote $\frac{3}{2}$ and others wrote $1\frac{1}{2}$, write both answers on the board. If only one of them comes up, introduce the other yourself.

Is there any other way you know to write $\frac{3}{2}$ [or $1\frac{1}{2}$]? Is $\frac{3}{2}$ greater than 1? Could you write $\frac{3}{2}$ in another way as a mixed number, using 1 and a fraction? [Or, is it possible to write $1\frac{1}{2}$ as a fraction? How many halves are in $1\frac{1}{2}$? Do you know a way to write a fraction that means three halves?]

When both forms are written on the board, ask students how they can represent $\frac{3}{2}$, using the 4×6 rectangle as a whole.

How could you use our 4×6 rectangles to make a picture for the fraction $\frac{3}{2}$? Let's say that these rectangles are sandwiches, and I ate $\frac{3}{2}$ of a sandwich. How could you show $\frac{3}{2}$ of a sandwich?

Distribute a copy of 4×6 Rectangles (M7) to each student.

① **Teacher Note:** Keeping Track of the Whole, p. 149

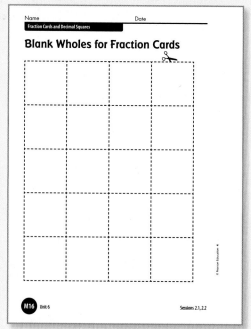

▲ Resource Masters, M16

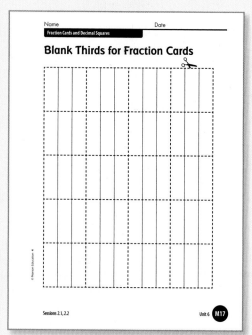

▲ Resource Masters, M17

Allow students a few minutes to work on showing $\frac{3}{2}$ with rectangles. As students continue working, ask questions such as:

Is $\frac{3}{2}$ more or less than 1? How do you know? How many halves are in 1 sandwich? How many halves are in $\frac{3}{2}$ of a sandwich? Does it help to look at the two different ways we wrote this fraction: $\frac{3}{2}$ and $1\frac{1}{2}$?

Keeping track of what represents 1 whole when working with fractions greater than 1 can be quite difficult for many students. ①

Ask students to share their ways of showing $\frac{3}{2}$ and to explain how their drawings show $\frac{3}{2}$. Use the context of sandwiches to help students clarify their ideas and to help students who may be less sure of how to represent $\frac{3}{2}$. Some students think of $\frac{3}{2}$ as 1 whole composed of two halves plus one more half. They are likely to show $\frac{3}{2}$ as follows:

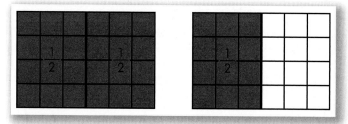

Other students think of $\frac{3}{2}$ as $\frac{1}{2} + \frac{1}{2} + \frac{1}{2}$. They may also show $\frac{3}{2}$ as 1 whole rectangle and $\frac{1}{2}$ of a second rectangle, or they sometimes show $\frac{3}{2}$ as $\frac{1}{2}$ of three rectangles.

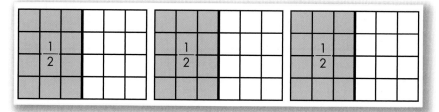

This representation also shows $\frac{3}{2}$ of a sandwich and in fact, represents more directly the meaning of $\frac{3}{2}$ as division. Students may think of it as showing each person's share if three sandwiches are divided equally between two people. If both of these representations come up, ask students to compare them.

Do both of these representations show $\frac{3}{2}$? If I eat the shaded parts in the first picture and my friend eats the shaded parts in the second picture, did we eat the same amount? How are the two pictures the same? (Both have $\frac{3}{2}$ of a sandwich shaded in.) How are they different? (The first picture shows two whole sandwiches with $\frac{1}{2}$ sandwich left over; the second picture shows three whole sandwiches with $1\frac{1}{2}$ sandwiches left over.)

- **Can students represent fractions that are more than one whole?** Can they represent mixed numbers? Can they represent fractions in which the numerator is greater than the denominator? Do they recognize that these fractions are more than 1?

- **Do students recognize some equivalent fractions, such as those that are equal to $\frac{1}{2}$, and use this understanding to create their representations?**

As you watch students work, ask them questions such as:

- How do you know that your picture represents [$\frac{3}{5}$, $\frac{3}{2}$, etc.]?

- If your picture shows $\frac{3}{5}$, show me $\frac{1}{5}$ on your rectangle.

- Which of these two fractions you just made is greater? How do you know?

DIFFERENTIATION: Supporting the Range of Learners

 **Intervention** As you circulate among the groups making cards, watch for problems students might have representing the fractions that are greater than 1. Some students have difficulty with fractions greater than 1 even if they were competent in their previous work with fractions less than 1. Help these students use a familiar context, such as thinking of the rectangles as sandwiches or brownies, to think through the meaning of fractions such as $\frac{5}{2}$. Also help them use their knowledge of fractions that equal 1, such as $\frac{2}{2}$. If $\frac{2}{2} = 1$, then how many whole rectangles are represented by $\frac{5}{2}$?

Encourage students who are having difficulty dividing the blank wholes to use the templates of rectangles with marked thirds and fifths.

SESSION FOLLOW-UP

3 Daily Practice and Homework

 Daily Practice: For ongoing review, have students complete *Student Activity Book* page 28.

 Homework: On *Student Activity Book* page 29, students practice adding fractions as they figure out what fraction is missing in an equation.

 Student Math Handbook: Students and families may use *Student Math Handbook* pages 53, 58 for reference and review. See pages 170–176 in the back of this unit.

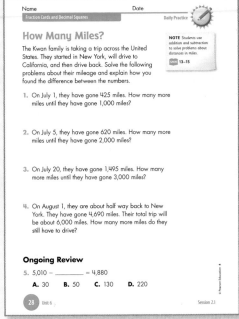

▲ Student Activity Book, p. 28

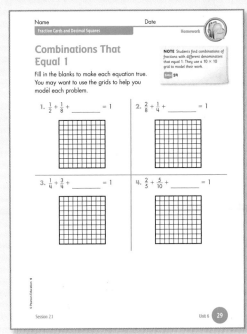

▲ Student Activity Book, p. 29

Fraction Cards, *continued*

Math Focus Points

◆ Finding fractional parts of a rectangular area

◆ Interpreting the meaning of the numerator and the denominator
of a fraction

Today's Plan		Materials
ACTIVITY **①Making Fraction Cards**	🕐 👥 **40 MIN GROUPS**	• *Student Activity Book,* pp. 26–27, 31 • M16 (as needed); M17 (as needed); M18 (as needed) • Colored oak tag or card stock; scissors; glue sticks; rulers; colored pencils or crayons
DISCUSSION **②One Piece Is Missing**	🕐 👥 👤 **20 MIN CLASS PAIRS**	
SESSION FOLLOW-UP **③Daily Practice**		• *Student Activity Book,* p. 32 • *Student Math Handbook,* pp. 56–57

Ten-Minute Math

Quick Survey For the survey, ask the class what languages they can speak or a different categorical question that you or the students choose. Make sure that they collect data about something they already know or can observe easily. With today's data, make a table.

What do you notice about the data? What do the data tell us about our class?

ACTIVITY

1 Making Fraction Cards

40 MIN GROUPS

Students continue making their set of Fraction Cards in their small groups.

In addition to the decks the groups make, you will need a class deck for the next few sessions. As groups finish their own decks, they can make cards for the class deck. You may wish to assign a column of fractions to each group. Choose a different identifying mark for the class deck and remind students to mark cards in the class deck with it.

When students finish making their portion of their group's deck, they work on *Student Activity Book* page 31. On this sheet, students identify fractions pictured as Fraction Cards and find an equivalent fraction for at least one of them.

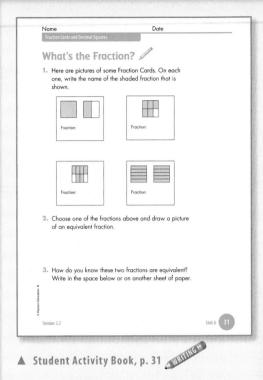

▲ **Student Activity Book, p. 31** *WRITING*

Students create Fraction Cards to help them interpret the meaning of the numerator and the denominator of a fraction.

ONGOING ASSESSMENT: Observing Students at Work

Students continue to draw representations of fractions that range from $\frac{0}{2}$ to $2\frac{1}{2}$, including fractions with numerators greater than denominators, such as $\frac{9}{6}$. See the Ongoing Assessment in Session 2.1, page 72.

Professional Development

① **Teacher Note:** Keeping Track of the Whole, p. 149

DIFFERENTIATION: Supporting the Range of Learners

Intervention If a group of students is having difficulty making representations for mixed numbers and for fractions greater than 1, you may want to meet with the students in a small group.①

2

DISCUSSION

One Piece Is Missing

20 MIN CLASS PAIRS

Math Focus Points for Discussion

- Interpreting the meaning of the numerator and the denominator of a fraction

Pose this problem to students:

A fourth grader was making Fraction Cards for $\frac{3}{4}$ and $\frac{5}{6}$, and said that she noticed something about both of them. She said that they both have "one piece missing," so they must be the same size. Do you agree with that? How would you make an argument for whether you agree or disagree?

First, what do you think she means by "one piece missing"?

Each fraction is one part away from a whole ($\frac{3}{4}$ plus one more fourth equals $\frac{4}{4}$, $\frac{5}{6}$ plus one more sixth equals $\frac{6}{6}$). Clarify this idea by sketching two rectangles to show that one part is missing to make each a whole.

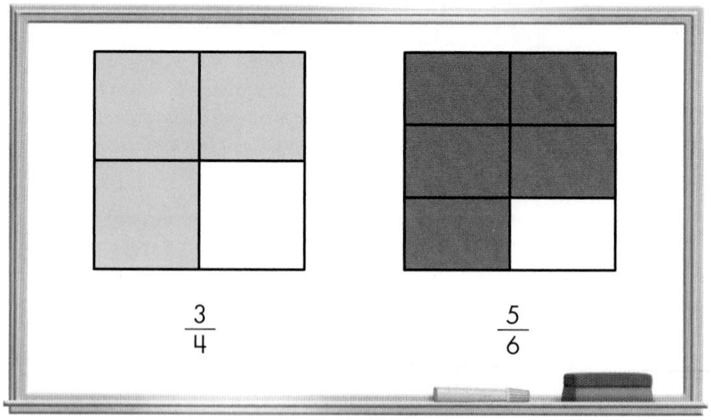

Students work with a partner to come up with an argument for whether $\frac{3}{4}$ and $\frac{5}{6}$ are the same size. Encourage students to use drawings and further examples of other fractions that have "one piece missing" (e.g., $\frac{7}{8}$, $\frac{2}{3}$) in their arguments. Give students about 10 minutes to work on this, and then bring them back together to discuss their thinking.

As students are making their arguments, listen with the following questions in mind:

- How do students compare fractions that are one fractional part less than 1? Do they begin with the understanding that both wholes in this case must be the same size? Do they try to keep the sizes of the parts the same and increase the size of the whole?

- Do they understand that $\frac{1}{6}$ and $\frac{1}{4}$ are different parts of the whole even though each is "one piece" of the whole? Do they see that the more equal parts you cut the whole into, the smaller each part? Do they think that sixths are bigger than fourths because the value of 6 is greater than that of 4?

- Can students make arguments based on their knowledge of the meaning of fractions, or do they rely on their drawings, which may or may not be accurate?

Before class ends, ask each student to write on a sheet of paper their ideas about whether $\frac{3}{4}$ is less than, equal to, or more than $\frac{5}{6}$ of the same whole. They should write their reasons for what they think and/or questions about what they do not understand. Collect these and read over them to get an idea of how students' reasoning about comparing fractions is developing.

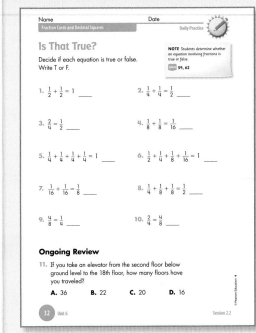
▲ **Student Activity Book, p. 32**

SESSION FOLLOW-UP

3 Daily Practice

Daily Practice: For reinforcement of this unit's content, have students complete *Student Activity Book* page 32.

Student Math Handbook: Students and families may use *Student Math Handbook* pages 56–57 for reference and review. See pages 170–176 in the back of this unit.

Capture Fractions

Math Focus Points

- Interpreting the meaning of the numerator and the denominator of a fraction
- Identifying equivalent fractions
- Ordering fractions and justifying their order through reasoning about fraction equivalencies and relationships

Today's Plan		Materials
1 DISCUSSION **Which Is Larger?**	20 MIN CLASS	• Fraction Cards posters*
2 ACTIVITY **Capture Fractions**	40 MIN GROUPS PAIRS	• *Student Activity Book*, p. 33 • M20*; M21* (as needed) • Connecting cubes (as needed)
3 SESSION FOLLOW-UP **Daily Practice and Homework**		• *Student Activity Book*, pp. 34–35 • *Student Math Handbook*, pp. 59–61; G1

*See *Materials to Prepare*, p. 65.

Ten-Minute Math

Quick Survey For the survey, ask the class what their favorite recess activity is or a different categorical question that you or the students choose. Make sure that they collect data about something they already know or can observe easily. Agree on a classification of 3 or 4 categories for the data and make a bar graph with the data.

What do you notice about the data? What do the data tell us about our class?

① Which Is Larger?

20 MIN   CLASS

Math Focus Points for Discussion

◆ Interpreting the meaning of the numerator and the denominator of a fraction

◆ Ordering fractions and justifying their order through reasoning about fraction equivalencies and relationships

This discussion focuses on using students' knowledge about fraction relationships and equivalencies to compare two fractions. ❶ ❷

Over the next couple of days, we will be using the Fraction Cards you made to play a new game called *Capture Fractions.* In this game, you will compare two fractions and decide which one is a larger portion of the whole (or of more than one whole). The player who has the larger fraction will take both cards.

Display the poster of the $\frac{1}{4}$ and $\frac{3}{5}$ Fraction Cards that you made ahead of time.

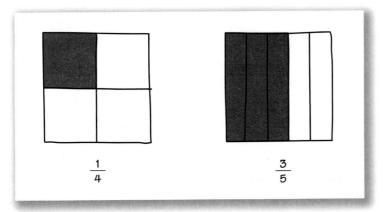

$$\frac{1}{4} \qquad\qquad \frac{3}{5}$$

Which fraction is larger, $\frac{1}{4}$ or $\frac{3}{5}$? You can use the pictures on the card to help you, but also think about what else you know about fractions to help you decide.

Listen for students' explanations that use what they know about the relationship between fifths and fourths or the relationships of $\frac{3}{5}$ and $\frac{1}{4}$ to other landmark fractions such as $\frac{1}{2}$.

When playing— discuss why $\frac{1}{2}$ is larger

Math Note

❶ **Comparing Fractions** In the next few sessions, as students put fractions in order, emphasize reasoning about the fractions rather than relying only on the drawings. The drawings on their Fraction Cards help students visualize the meaning of the numerator and denominator of the fraction and the relationship of each fraction to one whole. However, the pictures are helpful but not accurate enough to make judgments about all fraction comparisons, especially for fractions that are close in size. It is important that students use drawings and diagrams to visualize fractions but also that they understand that their drawings are approximations. More and more in Grades 4 and 5, students will visualize fractions and fraction relationships mentally. These mental images support students' understanding of the meaning of fractions as they learn to reason about fractions with their growing repertoire of fraction equivalencies.

Professional Development

❷ **Teacher Note:** Visualizing Fraction Equivalencies, p. 141

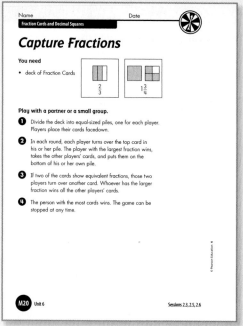
Students might say:

"I know that $\frac{3}{5}$ is bigger because $\frac{1}{4}$ is only a tiny bit bigger than $\frac{1}{5}$, but there are 3 of the fifths and only one of the fourths. So $\frac{3}{5}$ has to be more."

"$\frac{3}{5}$ is greater than $\frac{1}{2}$ because, if you look at a rectangle for fifths, you can see that it would take $2\frac{1}{2}$ of the fifths to equal $\frac{1}{2}$, so $\frac{3}{5}$ is larger. And we know that $\frac{1}{4}$ is less than $\frac{1}{2}$."

Now put up the poster of the $\frac{2}{3}$ and $\frac{5}{6}$ Fraction Cards.

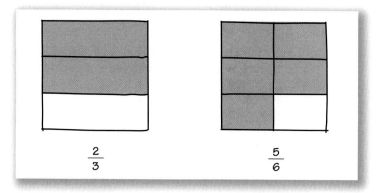

$$\frac{2}{3} \qquad\qquad \frac{5}{6}$$

Students might say:

"I can see from the picture that $\frac{2}{3}$ and $\frac{4}{6}$ are exactly equal. So $\frac{5}{6}$ is $\frac{1}{6}$ bigger than $\frac{2}{3}$."

"I know that sixths are smaller than thirds. $\frac{2}{3}$ is one-third away from a whole. $\frac{5}{6}$ is only a sixth away from a whole. So $\frac{5}{6}$ is closer to one whole because it is only a sixth away and that is smaller than a third."

ACTIVITY

2 Capture Fractions

40 MIN GROUPS PAIRS

Students continue to compare fractions by playing a new game, *Capture Fractions*. This game is modeled on the familiar card game War. In this version, the larger fraction wins each round. For a complete set of directions, refer to *Capture Fractions* (M20). Briefly demonstrate the game by playing one or two rounds with the class.

For the first game, have most students play in pairs so that they are comparing only two fractions at a time.

As students play, have each student record equivalent fractions that come up during the game on *Student Activity Book* page 33. If students fill *Student Activity Book* page 33, give them a copy of Finding Equivalent Fractions (M21).

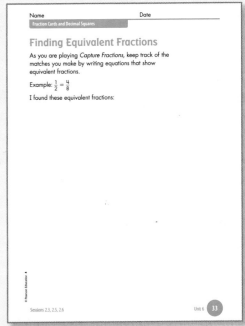

Name _____ Date _____
Fraction Cards and Decimal Squares

Finding Equivalent Fractions

As you are playing *Capture Fractions*, keep track of the matches you make by writing equations that show equivalent fractions.

Example: $\frac{1}{2} = \frac{4}{8}$

I found these equivalent fractions:

Sessions 2.3, 2.5, 2.6   Unit 6   33

▲ **Student Activity Book, p. 33;
Resource Masters, M21**

Professional Development

❸ **Teacher Note:** Strategies for Comparing Fractions, p. 151

Students continue to compare fractions by playing Capture Fractions.

ONGOING ASSESSMENT: Observing Students at Work

Students compare fractions to determine which is greater.

- **How do students decide which fraction is greater?** Do they use representations? Do they use reasoning based on fraction equivalencies that they know? Do they compare the fractions to landmark fractions such as $\frac{1}{2}$ or 1?

- **Do they pay attention to the value and meaning of both the numerator and denominator?**

- **Do students recognize equivalent fractions?**

Listen for the strategies that students are using and decide whether there are any you want students to share with the whole class during the next few sessions.❸

DIFFERENTIATION: Supporting the Range of Learners

Intervention Putting fractions into a context may help some students visualize the difference between the two fractions.

✱ Good practical application

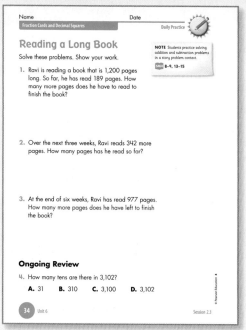

▲ Student Activity Book, p. 34

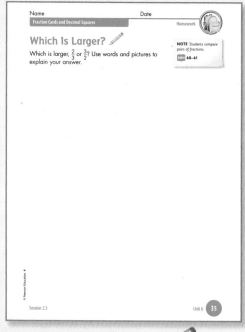

▲ Student Activity Book, p. 35

Imagine that four people are sharing one pizza, and five people are sharing another pizza that is the same size. If everyone gets one piece, which "pizza group" would you rather be part of, the group of four or the group of five? Which is a larger share: $\frac{1}{4}$ or $\frac{1}{5}$?

Imagine that I have a pack of sports cards that has 12 cards in it. I give you $\frac{8}{12}$ of my cards. How many cards do I give you? What if you have a pack of sports cards, with 12 just like mine, but instead you give me $\frac{3}{4}$ of your cards? Are you giving me more or fewer cards than I gave you? How could you figure it out?

Suggest that students draw pictures or divide a group of objects such as connecting cubes to represent the action of fraction problems.

Extension Some students who are fluent in comparing two fractions at a time can play the game with a group of three or four so that more fractions are considered in each round.

In another variation, each player puts down two cards and the players must decide who has the greater sum.

SESSION FOLLOW-UP

③ Daily Practice and Homework

 Daily Practice: For ongoing review, have students complete *Student Activity Book* page 34.

 Homework: On *Student Activity Book* page 35, students compare two fractions: $\frac{2}{3}$ and $\frac{3}{2}$. They write about their reasoning.

 Student Math Handbook: Students and families may use *Student Math Handbook* pages 59–61 and G1 for reference and review. See pages 170–176 in the back of this unit.

Comparing Fractions to Landmarks

Math Focus Points

◆ Identifying equivalent fractions

◆ Comparing fractions to the landmarks 0, $\frac{1}{2}$, 1, and 2

Vocabulary

landmarks

Today's Plan		Materials
ACTIVITY **1** **Comparing Fractions to Landmarks**	40 MIN · GROUPS · CLASS	• T68 • Landmark Cards*; Fraction Cards (from Session 2.3); chart: "Conjectures About Fractions"*
ACTIVITY **2** **Fractions in Containers**	20 MIN · INDIVIDUALS	• *Student Activity Book,* p. 37 • Fraction Cards (as needed)
SESSION FOLLOW-UP **3** **Daily Practice**		• *Student Activity Book,* p. 38 • *Student Math Handbook,* pp. 60–61

*See *Materials to Prepare,* p. 67.

Ten-Minute Math

Quick Survey For the survey, ask the class what was their main course for dinner last night or a different categorical question that you or the students choose. Make sure that they collect data about something they already know or can easily observe and that is likely to change on a different day. Agree on a classification of 3 or 4 categories for the data and make a bar graph. Keep the class data to use for comparison in the next session.

What do you notice about the data? What do the data tell us about our class?

ACTIVITY

① Comparing Fractions to Landmarks

40 MIN GROUPS CLASS

In this activity, students sequence fractions by comparing them to landmarks on a number line.

Pass out to each group of 4 students one set of Landmark Cards for 0, $\frac{1}{2}$, 1, and 2. Each group lays out its Landmark Cards in order on the floor, on a table, or on several desks pushed together, leaving space between each pair for other cards. Remind students about landmark numbers.

When else did you use landmarks this year? What numbers were those landmarks? (In the number and operations units; multiples of 10, 25, 100, and 1,000 were among the landmark numbers.) How are these numbers (0, $\frac{1}{2}$, 1, and 2) similar to the other landmarks? How are they different?

In their groups, students sort their Fraction Cards into seven piles as follows:

- Equal to 0
- Between 0 and $\frac{1}{2}$
- Equal to $\frac{1}{2}$
- Between $\frac{1}{2}$ and 1
- Equal to 1
- Between 1 and 2
- Equal to 2 or greater than 2

Cards that are equal to one of the Landmark Cards are put in a pile underneath that card, with the Landmark Card on top.❶

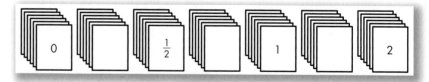

Placing their cards between landmarks requires students to compare many fractions to $\frac{1}{2}$. Students may reason about the relative size of these fractions in a variety of ways. As students are working, circulate among the groups and ask questions that require students to explain their reasoning about comparing fractions.

On the sheet of chart paper that you have titled "Conjectures About Fractions," start keeping a list of what students notice about comparing fractions.❷

Bring the class back together after most groups have completed sorting their cards. Ask each group to count the number of cards in each pile, and compare the results among the groups. Display the transparency Table for Grouping Fractions Between Landmarks (T68) and record fractions in their correct column as the class agrees on them.

You may want to collect data one column at a time because students may be rearranging their piles as they discuss their decisions with others. When students discover a fraction that is in one group's pile but not in another's, the class decides through discussion which placement is correct. Listen for the ways in which students are justifying whether a fraction is equivalent to one of the landmarks or between landmarks. In the last column, ask students to distinguish between fractions that are equal to 2 and fractions (or mixed numbers) that are greater than 2. ❸

✔ ONGOING ASSESSMENT: Observing Students at Work

Students compare fractions to the landmarks 0, $\frac{1}{2}$, 1, and 2.

- **How do students decide whether a fraction is less than $\frac{1}{2}$ or more than $\frac{1}{2}$?** What knowledge about the meaning of fractions and about fraction equivalencies do they use? Do they rely largely on the drawings on their fraction cards, or do they reason about the relationships between the fractions?

- **Do students recognize fractions that are equivalent to 0, 1, and 2?**

ACTIVITY

② Fractions in Containers

🕐 **20 MIN** 👤 **INDIVIDUALS**

For the rest of the session, students work individually on *Student Activity Book* page 37. In this activity, students determine the relationship of fractions to $\frac{1}{2}$ and 1. Pictures of containers filled with water to different heights provide a visual reference.

Professional Development

❸ **Dialogue Box:** Comparing Fractions to Landmarks, p. 165

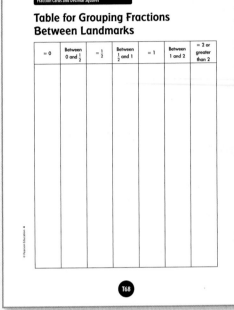

▲ Transparencies, T68

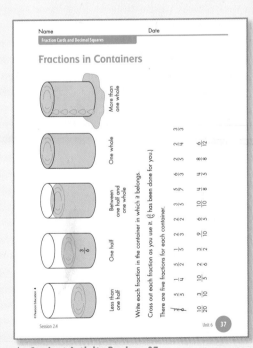

▲ Student Activity Book, p. 37

Students compare fractions to the landmarks $\frac{1}{2}$ and 1.

ONGOING ASSESSMENT: Observing Students at Work

Students sort fractions according to whether they are less than, more than, or equal to $\frac{1}{2}$ and 1.

- **Can students sort the fractions by reasoning about fraction equivalencies and other fraction relationships they know?** For example, "I know $\frac{3}{6}$ is equal to $\frac{1}{2}$ because $\frac{6}{6}$ equal 1 whole and 3 pieces is half of all the pieces, so it is half of the whole."

- **Are some groups of these fractions easier for students to sort than others?** Which fractions do they have to think more about?

As you watch students work, ask them questions such as these:

- How do you know that $\frac{4}{5}$ is between $\frac{1}{2}$ and 1? How many fifths would be equal to $\frac{1}{2}$? How many fifths would be exactly one whole?

- How do you know that $\frac{4}{8}$ is equal to $\frac{1}{2}$? Can you draw a picture to show why it is true?

DIFFERENTIATION: Supporting the Range of Learners

Intervention This activity provides an opportunity for students who have been working collaboratively to demonstrate their own understanding of how to sort fractions with respect to landmarks. If some students are having difficulty doing this task on their own, ask them to work with one category at a time. It may help them to sort through their fraction cards for all the cards that are equivalent to $\frac{1}{2}$.

Then they can look at the list of fractions on *Student Activity Book* page 37 to see whether they recognize any of those fractions.

You may also ask students to draw as many fractions equal to $\frac{1}{2}$ as they can. If necessary, provide some starters—for example, quickly sketch a rectangle with four equal parts, another with eight parts, and a third with 12 parts. Ask students to show half the rectangle on each one and then to write a fraction for their drawing. Finally, after they have checked their fractions with you, they can look for them in the list on *Student Activity Book* page 37.

SESSION FOLLOW-UP

3 Daily Practice

 Daily Practice: For reinforcement of this unit's content, have students complete *Student Activity Book* page 38.

 Student Math Handbook: Students and families may use *Student Math Handbook* pages 60–61 for reference and review. See pages 170–176 in the back of this unit.

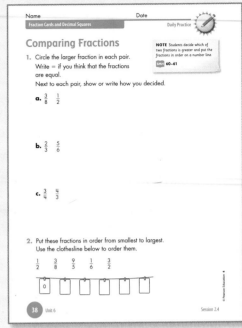

▲ Student Activity Book, p. 38

Fractions on a Number Line

Math Focus Points

◆ Ordering fractions and justifying their order through reasoning about fraction equivalencies and relationships

◆ Representing fractions using a number line

◆ Comparing fractions to the landmarks 0, $\frac{1}{2}$, 1, and 2

Today's Plan		Materials
1 DISCUSSION **Comparing $\frac{3}{8}$ and $\frac{2}{4}$**	20 MIN CLASS PAIRS	• $\frac{3}{8}$ and $\frac{2}{4}$ Fraction Cards (from the class deck)
2 ACTIVITY **Introducing Fractions on a Number Line**	15 MIN CLASS	• Class Fraction Number Line*; class deck of Fraction Cards; Fraction Cards; adding machine tape* (optional); chart: "Conjectures About Fractions"
3 MATH WORKSHOP **Comparing Fractions** **3A** *Making a Fraction Number Line* **3B** *Capture Fractions*	25 MIN	**3A** • *Student Activity Book,* p. 39 • Class Fraction Number Line; class deck of Fraction Cards; Fraction Cards; adding machine tape (optional) **3B** • M20; M21 (as needed) • Connecting cubes (as needed)
4 SESSION FOLLOW-UP **Daily Practice and Homework**		• *Student Activity Book,* pp. 40–41 • *Student Math Handbook,* pp. 60–61; G1

*See *Materials to Prepare,* p. 67.

Ten-Minute Math

Quick Survey For the survey, collect data about the same question you used in the previous session (What was your main course for dinner last night?). Add today's data to the bar graph created in the last session and ask students to make comparisons.

What do you notice about our data today? How are the data the same as last session's?

How are they different? What does that tell us about our class?

DISCUSSION

1 Comparing $\frac{3}{8}$ and $\frac{2}{4}$

Math Focus Points for Discussion

◆ Comparing fractions to the landmarks 0, $\frac{1}{2}$, 1, and 2

Today we'll be putting fractions in order from the least to the greatest. Sometimes it's easy to tell whether one fraction is greater than another. Who remembers playing a hand in *Capture Fractions* when you knew right away which fraction was greater?

Students might say:

"If one of the cards is more than 1 and the other is less than 1, the 'more than 1 card' is bigger."

"It's easy if it's something like one half and three halves because you know that three halves has more pieces."

From the class deck of Fraction Cards, show students the two cards that have $\frac{3}{8}$ and $\frac{2}{4}$ represented.

How can I tell which is larger: $\frac{3}{8}$ or $\frac{2}{4}$?

Students work in pairs for a few minutes on this problem. Encourage them to draw representations to support their ideas. Listen for students who are comparing each fraction to landmarks. Ask questions such as the following:

Can you compare either of these fractions to a landmark? What landmarks are they close to? How close are they?

Could these two fractions be equal? Why or why not?

When most students have made some progress comparing these two fractions, bring the class back together, even if not every pair has come to a conclusion. Collect several ideas from students, being sure to include ideas about equivalent fractions and the relationship of the two fractions to $\frac{1}{2}$ (e.g., that $\frac{2}{4} = \frac{4}{8}$ and that $\frac{3}{8} < \frac{4}{8}$).

Professional Development

❶ **Teacher Note:** Strategies for Comparing Fractions, p. 151

If most students are comfortable comparing $\frac{3}{8}$ and $\frac{2}{4}$, pose a more difficult comparison, such as $\frac{1}{8}$ and $\frac{2}{5}$, in which the denominators are not so closely related and neither of the fractions equals $\frac{1}{2}$. If it seems to you that students could benefit from another comparison of about the same level of difficulty as this one, ask them to compare $\frac{5}{6}$ and $\frac{2}{3}$.

Students will think more about these comparisons and about general ideas they are formulating for comparing fractions as they work on the next activity, ordering fractions on a number line.❶

ACTIVITY

15 MIN   CLASS

② Introducing Fractions on a Number Line

In this activity, students work in pairs to order Fraction Cards in sequence on their own number lines, using half of their group's deck. At the same time, small groups of students take turns placing a few of the cards in the class set on a class Fraction Number Line.

Begin the class Fraction Number Line with the two fractions that students just discussed: $\frac{2}{4}$ and $\frac{3}{8}$.

Over the next two days, we're going to make a class number line with all of the fractions in our Fraction Cards deck. Instead of just placing them between the right landmarks, we're going to try to put them all in order. We'll still use the landmarks we used in the last session to help us think about where the other fractions go.

Who would like to place these two cards on the number line I've started here? Will $\frac{2}{4}$ come before or after $\frac{1}{2}$ on the line? Where does $\frac{3}{8}$ go?

When the class has agreed on the correct placement of these two fractions, draw two or three more cards from the class deck and have student volunteers come up and place them. Make sure that at least one of the fractions is equivalent to one already placed. Demonstrate placing these equivalent Fraction Cards in a column, as shown below:

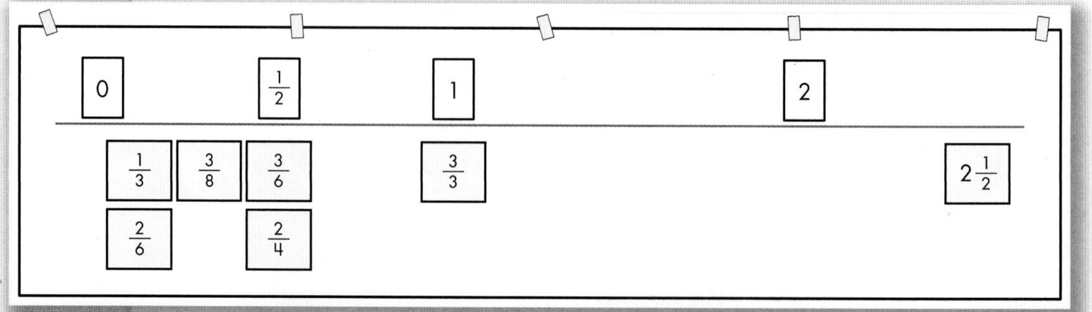

0	$\frac{1}{2}$	1		2
$\frac{1}{3}$ $\frac{3}{8}$ $\frac{3}{6}$		$\frac{3}{3}$		$2\frac{1}{2}$
$\frac{2}{6}$ $\frac{2}{4}$				

Handwritten margin notes:
Can do # line on wall
Sticky notes —
hang equivalent
fractions punch
hole
use paper clip

If a Fraction Card is drawn that students are unsure about where to place, leave it out for now, and invite students to think about this fraction as they make their own number lines.

Explain to students that during Math Workshop, they will be working in pairs with only half of their Fraction Cards deck at a time (each group of four divides into groups of two, and each pair uses half of the deck). They may either lay out a strip of adding machine tape to represent their group's number line or simply lay cards out on their work space between and on top of the Landmark Cards that they used in Session 2.4. If you have floor space available, students will have more flexibility than if they use the tops of their desks. Each pair needs about six feet of space.

Ask students to keep track of any general rules they are formulating. For example, when students compared $\frac{3}{8}$ and $\frac{4}{8}$, some students may have talked about how, if the denominators are the same (or "if the number of pieces is the same"), the fraction with the smaller numerator is smaller. Any conjectures such as this one can be added to the class chart of conjectures about fractions.❷

Teaching Note

❷ **Limited Space** If space is limited, decide how you will orchestrate this activity so that only a few groups are making their number lines at a time, perhaps in a designated area in the classroom. In the meantime, other students can play *Capture Fractions* or place more cards on the class Fraction Number Line.

MATH WORKSHOP
③ Comparing Fractions

25 MIN

Students work on two activities that focus on comparing fractions and identifying equivalent fractions. They will continue to work on these activities in Session 2.6.

Because students need their Fraction Cards deck for both activities, each group of four will need to decide how they will share the cards. One pair may use the deck to play *Capture Fractions* while the other students in the group work on making a Fraction Number Line.

③A Making a Fraction Number Line

PAIRS

Students divide their deck of Fraction Cards in half and plan how they will put one half of the deck (20 cards) in order from the smallest fraction to the largest. They use 0, $\frac{1}{2}$, 1, and 2 as landmarks which they can write on a strip of adding machine tape or use their Landmark Cards. You may suggest that students first sort their cards into the 7 piles they used in Session 2.4 (equal to 0, between 0 and $\frac{1}{2}$, equal to $\frac{1}{2}$, and so on) and then work on ordering each pile.

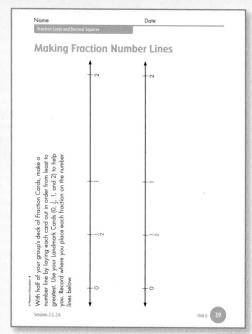

Name _____ Date _____

Fraction Cards and Decimal Squares

Making Fraction Number Lines

With half of your group's deck of Fraction Cards, make a number line by laying each card out in order from least to greatest. Use your Landmark Cards (0, $\frac{1}{2}$, 1, and 2) to help you. Record where you place each fraction on the number lines below.

© Pearson Education 4

Sessions 2.5, 2.6

Unit 6   39

▲ **Student Activity Book, p. 39**

After each pair has sorted its half of the deck, the students switch cards and repeat the activity with the second half of their deck of Fraction Cards. They record each number line that they make on *Student Activity Book* page 39.

Students also go to the class Fraction Number Line and place several cards from the class deck on the display. They may refer to their own number lines, and need to consider the fractions that have already been placed. Decide how many cards each small group will place. You may want to assign certain fractions to certain groups. You may also assign different tasks to each group, such as finding all the fractions that are equal to $\frac{1}{2}$, or finding all the cards that are equal to 2 or larger than 2. If groups have questions about cards that have already been placed, they may flag those cards in some way, perhaps with a self-stick note.

Students place their Fraction Cards onto a number line.

ONGOING ASSESSMENT: Observing Students at Work

Students order fractions on a number line.

- **How do students order fractions?** Do they use landmarks? Can they identify equivalent fractions?

- **How do students decide about the order of fractions that are close in size but have different denominators?** Do they use representations? Do they reason about their relationships to landmark fractions?

As you talk with students, ask them to explain their reasoning and be alert for any general claims that students are formulating. Remember these for later discussion.

DIFFERENTIATION: Supporting the Range of Learners

Intervention Some students may need to work with a smaller set of fractions, perhaps in related groups such as halves, fourths, and eighths or thirds, sixths, and twelfths.

Extension Students who are ready for more of a challenge may add other fractions of their own choosing to the class number line. You may also suggest some more challenging fractions, such as fractions that are not equivalent to any of the others in the list, such as $\frac{7}{12}$, $\frac{11}{12}$, or $\frac{17}{12}$; fractions with denominators that they have not yet encountered but that are related to some of the fractions they know, such as $\frac{1}{9}$, $\frac{3}{9}$, $\frac{4}{9}$, and $\frac{8}{9}$; or fractions with unfamiliar denominators that are not related to fractions they have encountered so far, such as $\frac{1}{7}$, $\frac{4}{7}$, and $\frac{6}{7}$.

. . . .

3B Capture Fractions

PAIRS

Students continue to play the game *Capture Fractions*, in which each player puts down one Fraction Card and both players decide which fraction is greater. For complete details about this activity, see Session 2.3, pages 80–81.

SESSION FOLLOW-UP
4 Daily Practice and Homework

 Daily Practice: For ongoing review, have students complete *Student Activity Book* page 40.

 Homework: On *Student Activity Book* page 41, students determine whether combinations of fractions are more or less than 1. You may want to review the symbols for less than (<) and greater than (>) before this homework.

 Student Math Handbook: Students and families may use *Student Math Handbook* pages 60–61 and G1 for reference and review. See pages 170–176 in the back of this unit.

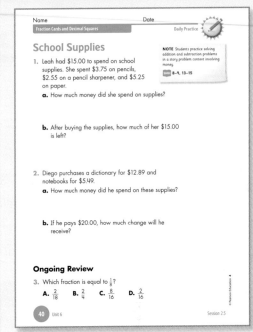

▲ Student Activity Book, p. 40

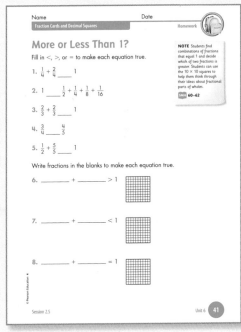

▲ Student Activity Book, p. 41

Assessment: Comparing Fractions

Math Focus Points

◆ Ordering fractions and justifying their order through reasoning about fraction equivalencies and relationships

◆ Representing fractions using a number line

◆ Comparing fractions to the landmarks 0, $\frac{1}{2}$, 1, and 2

Today's Plan		Materials
ASSESSMENT ACTIVITY ① **Comparing Fractions** ✓ 🕐 15 MIN 👤 INDIVIDUALS		• M23*
MATH WORKSHOP ② **Comparing Fractions** ②A Making a Fraction Number Line ②B *Capture Fractions* 🕐 30 MIN		②A • *Student Activity Book*, p. 39 • Class Fraction Number Line; class deck of Fraction Cards; Fraction Cards; adding machine tape (optional) ②B • M20; M21 (from Session 2.3) • Connecting cubes (as needed)
DISCUSSION ③ **Reviewing the Class Fraction Number Line** 🕐 15 MIN 👥 CLASS		• Class Fraction Number Line; class deck of Fraction Cards; chart: "Conjectures About Fractions"
SESSION FOLLOW-UP ④ **Daily Practice and Homework**		• *Student Activity Book*, p. 43 • *Student Math Handbook*, pp. 60–61; G1

*See *Materials to Prepare*, p. 67.

Ten-Minute Math

Quick Survey For the survey, ask the class to choose a question that will result in numerical data (that is, a question for which each person responds with a quantity, such as "How many brothers and sisters do you have?"). With today's data, make a line plot.

What do you notice about the data? What do the data tell us about our class?

ASSESSMENT ACTIVITY

Comparing Fractions

15 MIN INDIVIDUALS

On Assessment: Comparing Fractions (M23), students solve three problems about comparing pairs of fractions. This assessment focuses on Benchmark 4: Order fractions with like and unlike denominators. ❶ ❷

Students work on this sheet individually. As students finish the assessment, they can work on Math Workshop activities.

Students complete the assessment activity that focuses on fractions.

DIFFERENTIATION: Supporting the Range of Learners

ELL Some English Language Learners may understand the task but may have difficulty putting their explanations in writing. Support these students by asking questions about the representations they made. Then restate their responses and help them translate their oral responses into written form.

MATH WORKSHOP

Comparing Fractions

30 MIN

Students continue to work on the Math Workshop activities from Session 2.5.

❷ᴬ Making a Fraction Number Line

PAIRS

For complete details about this activity, see Session 2.5, pages 90–92.

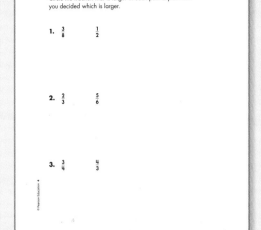

Name _____ Date _____

Fraction Cards and Decimal Squares

Assessment: Comparing Fractions

Circle the fraction that is larger in each pair. Explain how you decided which is larger.

1. $\frac{3}{8}$ $\frac{1}{2}$

2. $\frac{2}{3}$ $\frac{5}{6}$

3. $\frac{3}{4}$ $\frac{4}{3}$

© Pearson Education 4

Session 2.6   Unit 6 **M23**

 ▲ **Resource Masters, M23**   PORTFOLIO

Math Note

❶ **Assuming the Same Whole in the Assessment** Let students know that these pairs of fractions are assumed to be fractions of the same whole. Sometimes students explain that it is impossible to compare these fractions because "$\frac{3}{8}$ of a table cannot be compared with $\frac{1}{2}$ of an ant" or "$\frac{3}{4}$ of 2 is, in fact, more than $\frac{4}{3}$ of 1". Note that these students are bringing up a very important understanding about comparing fractions, but explain that in this case, all the fractions are related to the same whole.

Professional Development

❷ **Teacher Note:** Assessment: Comparing Fractions, p. 153

2B *Capture Fractions*

PAIRS

For complete details about this activity, see Session 2.3, pages 80–81.

DISCUSSION

Reviewing the Class Fraction Number Line

15 MIN   CLASS

Math Focus Points for Discussion

◆ Ordering fractions and justifying their order through reasoning about fraction equivalencies and relationships

Bring the class together when the class Fraction Number Line is nearly complete, perhaps with only a few cards left that students were not sure about.

What helped you make decisions about where to put the fractions on the number line? Which fractions were easy to place? Which were hard?

If there are cards that have not yet been placed on the class number line, have the class discuss where to put those cards. Encourage students to make arguments for why they think a fraction should go where they are suggesting by using knowledge of equivalent fractions and other strategies based on the meaning of fractions.

Refer to the list of class conjectures about fractions and choose one or two to discuss at greater length. You might choose conjectures about the following:

- Pairs of fractions with the same denominator and different numerators (e.g., $\frac{2}{5}$ and $\frac{4}{5}$)

- Pairs of fractions with the same numerator and different denominators (e.g., $\frac{2}{5}$ and $\frac{2}{6}$)

- Pairs of fractions in which the numerator and denominator of one are double the numerator and denominator of the other (e.g., $\frac{2}{3}$ and $\frac{4}{6}$)

- Using the relationship of the numerator to denominator to decide whether a fraction is less than or more than $\frac{1}{2}$ or less than or more than 1 (e.g., if the numerator is less than half the denominator, the fraction is less than $\frac{1}{2}$)

As students make their arguments, draw representations on the board to help other students visualize their thinking. However, ask questions that encourage students to rely on what they know about fraction relationships and the relationships of fractions to landmarks such as $\frac{1}{2}$ and 1, not only on how the pictures look. For example, if the class is discussing pairs of fractions with the same numerator but different denominators (e.g., $\frac{2}{5}$ and $\frac{2}{6}$), ask the following questions:

*How do you know that $[\frac{2}{6}]$ is a smaller amount than $[\frac{2}{5}]$? What do the [5] and [6] tell you about these fractions? What do the two [2s] tell you? Are there other pairs of fractions like this for which you could use the same strategy? Is there a general rule you can put into words about pairs of fractions like this? How do you know that your rule will always work?*❸

Professional Development

❸ **Dialogue Box:** Conjectures About Fractions, p. 167

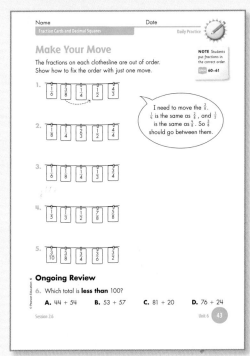

▲ **Student Activity Book, p. 43**

Students order fractions and justify their order through reasoning about fraction equivalencies and relationships.

SESSION FOLLOW-UP

4 **Daily Practice and Homework**

 Daily Practice: For reinforcement of this unit's content, have students complete *Student Activity Book* page 43.

 Homework: For homework, students choose one of the fraction conjectures on your class list that they are convinced is true and write an argument to show why it is true. They should use representations to illustrate their arguments. Make sure that students copy one of the conjectures on blank paper to take home.

 Student Math Handbook: Students and families may use *Student Math Handbook* pages 60–61 and G1 for reference and review. See pages 170–176 in the back of this unit.

Mathematical Emphases

Rational Numbers Understanding the meaning of fractions and decimal fractions

Math Focus Points

◆ Identifying everyday uses of fractions and decimals

◆ Reading and writing tenths and hundredths

◆ Representing tenths and hundredths as parts of an area

Rational Numbers Comparing the values of fractions and decimal fractions

Math Focus Points

◆ Ordering decimals and justifying their order through reasoning about representations and the meaning of the numbers

◆ Identifying decimal and fraction equivalents

Computation with Rational Numbers Using representations to add rational numbers

Math Focus Points

◆ Using representations to combine tenths and hundredths

◆ Estimating sums of decimal numbers

◆ Adding decimal numbers that are multiples of 0.1 and 0.25 (e.g., 2.3 + 3.25)

Working with Decimals

	Student Activity Book	Student Math Handbook	Professional Development: Read Ahead of Time	
SESSION 3.1 p. 104				
Representing Decimals Students list everyday uses of fractions and decimals. They are introduced to reading and writing tenths and hundredths. They relate these numbers to equivalent fractions and represent them as parts of a 10 × 10 square.	44–47	64–68	• **Teacher Note:** Extending Place Value to Tenths and Hundredths, p. 157	
SESSION 3.2 p. 111				
Comparing Decimals Students represent decimal fractions on a 10 × 10 square in order to decide which of two numbers is larger. They play a game in which they compare decimals by representing them or by reasoning about the meaning of the numbers.	49–50	69; G4		
SESSION 3.3 p. 116				
Representing and Combining Decimals Students compare equivalent fractions and decimal fractions $(0.3, \frac{3}{10}, \frac{30}{100})$. They use representations to combine decimal fractions as they play *Fill Two*.	51	69; G7	• **Dialogue Box:** Are These Equal?, p. 169	
SESSION 3.4 p. 120				
Estimating and Adding Miles and Tenths of a Mile Students estimate and add distances in miles and tenths and hundredths of a mile in the context of running or walking.	52–55	70–71		
SESSION 3.5 p. 127				
Comparing and Combining Decimals Through Math Workshop activities, students work on identifying, representing, and combining numbers that include tenths and hundredths.	57–59	70–71; G4, G7		

Materials to Gather	Materials to Prepare
• **T69–T70, Decimal Grids** 🖨	• **Chart paper** Prepare a chart titled "Everyday Uses of Fractions, Everyday Uses of Decimals." • **M15, 10 × 10 Squares** Make copies. (6 copies per student, additional as needed; the 10 × 10 Squares will be used during the rest of the Investigation)
• **M15, 10 × 10 Squares** (from Session 3.1) • **T67, 10 × 10 Squares** 🖨	• **M27, *Decimal Compare*** Review directions for *Decimal Compare*. Make copies. (as needed) • **M26, Decimal Cards** Make copies. (1 per student) Use cardstock for more durable sets. Enlist the help of parents or have students cut out the cards outside math time. • **T71, Decimal Cards** 🖨 Cut out each card to make one transparent set.
• **M15, 10 × 10 Squares** (from Session 3.1) • **M26, Decimal Cards** (from Session 3.2) • **T67, 10 × 10 Squares** 🖨 (from Session 3.2) • **Colored pencils, crayons, or markers** (as needed) • **T71, Decimal Cards** 🖨 (from Session 3.2)	• **M28, *Fill Two*** Review the directions for *Fill Two*. Make copies. (as needed)
• **M15, 10 × 10 Squares** (as needed)	• **Choose a destination** Choose a destination that is 1–3 miles from the school that you think is familiar to your students (a library, a community landmark, a store or restaurant, a park). If you can, measure the distance yourself to let students know the exact measurement. If not, simply estimate.
• **M15, 10 × 10 Squares** (from Session 3.1) • **M26, Decimal Cards** (from Session 3.2) • **T72–T73, Make a Running Log** 🖨 • **Colored pencils, crayons, or markers** (as needed)	

🖨 Overhead Transparency

Working with Decimals,
continued

	Student Activity Book	Student Math Handbook	Professional Development: Read Ahead of Time
SESSION 3.6 p. 132			
Comparing and Combining Decimals, *continued* Students continue to work on identifying, representing, and combining numbers that include tenths and hundredths.	57–58, 60	69–71; G4, G7	
SESSION 3.7 p. 135			
End-of-Unit Assessment Students are assessed on the benchmarks of this unit by completing problems that require them to compare and order fractions and decimals.	61	60–61, 69	• **Teacher Note:** End-of-Unit Assessment, p. 159

Materials to Gather	Materials to Prepare
• **M15, 10 × 10 Squares** (from Session 3.1) • **M26, Decimal Cards** (from Session 3.2) • **Colored pencils, crayons, or markers** (as needed)	
	• **M31, End-of-Unit Assessment** Make copies. (1 per student)

Representing Decimals

Math Focus Points

- Identifying everyday uses of fractions and decimals
- Reading and writing tenths and hundredths
- Representing tenths and hundredths as parts of an area

Vocabulary
decimal

Today's Plan		Materials
① DISCUSSION **Everyday Uses of Fractions and Decimals**	15 MIN CLASS	• Chart: "Everyday Uses of Fractions, Everyday Uses of Decimals"*
② ACTIVITY **Introducing Decimals**	20 MIN CLASS PAIRS	• T69–T70
③ ACTIVITY **Decimals on the 10 × 10 Square**	25 MIN PAIRS	• *Student Activity Book,* pp. 44–45 • M15*
④ SESSION FOLLOW-UP **Daily Practice and Homework**		• *Student Activity Book,* pp. 46–47 • *Student Math Handbook,* pp. 64–68

*See *Materials to Prepare,* p. 101.

Ten-Minute Math

Practicing Place Value Write 0.1 on the board and have students practice saying it. Let students know that this number is commonly read both as "one tenth" and as "point 1." Make sure all students can read, write, and say this number correctly. Ask:

- What is one-tenth more than 0.1? What is 0.2 more? What is 0.5 more? What is 1 more?

Write each answer on the board. Ask students to compare each sum with 0.1. Which places have the same digits? Which do not? Why? If time remains, pose additional similar problems using these numbers: 0.3 and 0.4.

15 MIN   CLASS

1 Everyday Uses of Fractions and Decimals

Math Focus Points for Discussion

◆ Identifying everyday uses of fractions and decimals

We have just spent some time thinking about and working with fractions. Now we are going to think about and work with another kind of number called **decimals**. All our numbers are called decimal numbers because *decimal* means 10, and our number system is based on tens. What do you think I mean when I say that our number system is based on tens?

Briefly ask students to think about their work with the place value of numbers. They should have ideas about our numbers: that ten ones make one 10, ten tens make one 100, ten hundreds make one 1,000, and so forth.

Then introduce the idea that numbers (or parts of numbers) less than 1 can also be written in this system.

You're very used to writing numbers that are less than 1, such as $\frac{1}{2}$ or $\frac{3}{4}$, by using fractions. You probably know that you can also write numbers less than 1 by using a decimal point in our base-ten system. These numbers are like fractions: they identify quantities that are *between* whole numbers. I know that you have seen these numbers in various places and that you studied a bit about decimal numbers less than 1 in Grade 3. Does anyone know how to say or write any of these numbers?

Accept a few examples from students. If students do not have any knowledge of decimals, put up a few examples that are likely to be recognizable, such as 0.5, 1.5, or 0.25. Briefly ask students a few questions about what they know about the values of each of these numbers. Do they know fractions that they are equal to? Are they more or less than 1? This conversation will give you a sense of students' knowledge and experience with decimal fractions.

Display the chart you prepared for listing everyday uses of fractions and decimals.

Can anyone give us an example of a fraction or decimal that you see or hear at home, at the store, or somewhere else?

As students suggest uses, record them under the appropriate heading. If they give you only a number, encourage them to give a real-life context for its use. If they mention a use, ask for an example of a number they might see in that use. If they have difficulty doing this, provide a few of your own examples.

You've suggested that 0.5 is a decimal. Where might you see this sort of number used? I see it in a car odometer that shows how many miles the car has traveled or on a digital thermometer. If you're sick and someone takes your temperature, do you know what the normal body temperature is? (about 98.6 degrees)

Add to the list as many examples as your class can come up with in 5 to 10 minutes.

Everyday Uses of Fractions	Everyday Uses of Decimals
$\frac{1}{2}$ of a sandwich	$9.75
a quarter of an hour	1.5 pounds
$\frac{3}{4}$ inch	.346 batting average
$1\frac{1}{2}$ lbs of sliced cheese	14.567 gallons of gas on the gas pump
	10.5 miles on the car's odometer

DIFFERENTIATION: Supporting the Range of Learners

ELL Make sure that the task is clear by providing two or three concrete examples of the use of fractions and decimals in everyday life—for example, a set of measuring spoons used for baking and an item with a price tag attached. Some English Language Learners may lack the necessary vocabulary to share their ideas. Have magazines and newspapers available and encourage those students to find pictures of examples they can share. Then provide vocabulary support as needed.

As you list examples of decimals, ask a few more questions to assess what your students know.

Can you say 1.5 pounds in a different way? What mixed number is equivalent to 1.5?

How much is 14.567 gallons of gas? What amounts of gas is it between? (Students might say "It's more than 14 gallons and less than 15 gallons"; some students might know it's more than $14\frac{1}{2}$ gallons.)

Is $9.75 a decimal? (Yes, it means 9 dollars and $\frac{75}{100}$ or $\frac{3}{4}$ of a dollar. One penny is $\frac{1}{100}$ of a dollar.)

At this point, students' familiarity with decimals may be quite varied. Be alert to any misconceptions they might have and plan to address these as this Investigation progresses.

ACTIVITY

2 Introducing Decimals

20 MIN   CLASS   PAIRS

Place the transparencies of Decimal Grids (T69–T70) on the overhead.

Let's use this blank square to represent one whole. You can think of it as a square piece of cloth, a pan of cornbread, a piece of land on which you're going to plant a garden, or something else that you can imagine cutting up. The other grids show the same square divided into equal parts. Let's say that I shaded in one part of Grid A. What part have I shaded in? How would you write that amount?❶

Students should be able to tell you that one way to write this amount is as the fraction $\frac{1}{10}$. Ask students whether they know how to write one tenth as a decimal. If they do not know, show them yourself.

The place to the right of the decimal point is for tenths. If there is a 1 in that place, it means one tenth. I can write it with a zero in the ones place to show that there are no whole numbers, or I can just write the decimal point followed by the 1. Both of these are ways to write one tenth.❷

What if I shaded in five of these parts on the first grid? How much of the whole square would that be? It's one half, but how else could you name it? How would you write five tenths?

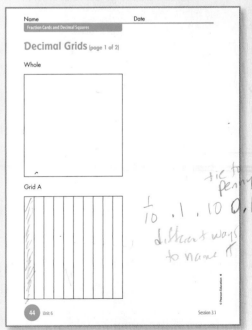

▲ Student Activity Book, p. 44; Resource Masters, M24; T69

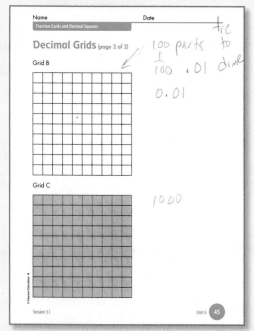

▲ **Student Activity Book, p. 45; Resource Masters, M25; T70**

Now allow students a few minutes to look at the other two grids. Ask them to figure out how many parts Grids B and C are divided into (100 and 1,000 parts, respectively) and to see what else they notice when they compare all four squares. Then ask students some questions about identifying and naming parts of Grids B and C.

How many parts is Grid B divided into? What would you call one part of this grid if the whole square is one whole? How would you write that as a fraction? Does anyone know how to write it as a decimal? How many of these hundredths equal one tenth?

Repeat these questions with Grid C, divided into thousandths. You should end up with a list on the board or chart paper of fraction and decimal notations for these amounts. Also write the words and make sure that students see and hear the difference between *ten* and *tenth*, between *hundred* and *hundredth*, and between *thousand* and *thousandth*.

$\frac{1}{10}$	0.1	.1	one tenth
$\frac{5}{10}$	0.5	.5	five tenths
$\frac{1}{100}$	0.01	.01	one hundredth
$\frac{1}{1000}$	0.001	.001	one thousandth

As students share what they notice about the grids, emphasize how these decimal places extend the place-value system and how each place is ten times the next place to the right, just as with the whole numbers: ten tenths equal 1; ten hundredths equal one tenth; ten thousandths equal one hundredth.❸ ❹

ACTIVITY

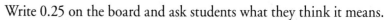

3 Decimals on the 10 × 10 Square

25 MIN PAIRS

Write 0.25 on the board and ask students what they think it means.

What number do you think this is? How would you say it? How would you color it in on one of these grids?

Students can talk in pairs for a minute about these questions. Then ask for their ideas. Some students may say that this number is "two tenths and five hundredths," which is correct. This may be clearer for some students than the way we conventionally say this number, *twenty-five hundredths*.

Jill was saying that there is a 2 in the tenths place, which means two tenths, and a 5 in the hundredths place, which means five hundredths. I agree that this number is 2 tenths and 5 hundredths. The way this number is usually read is "25 hundredths." Is 2 tenths and 5 hundredths also equal to 25 hundredths?

As a way to answer this question, ask students to color in the right number of squares for 0.25 on both Grid A and Grid B on *Student Activity Book* page 44. They can work with a partner to discuss how much to color before they actually do it. If some students finish quickly, give them a copy of 10 × 10 Squares (M15) and ask them to shade in 0.5 and 0.75.

Ask students what they noticed about shading in 0.25. Also ask what was difficult or confusing about shading in this amount.

Students might say:

"It's 25 out of 100 squares, so it's the same as one-fourth."

"I didn't know how to do it on the tenths grid, so I did it on the hundredths first. Then I could see that it was two tenths and half of another tenth."

"At first I shaded in two tenths on Grid A and five hundredths on Grid B, but then you were saying that I had to do the whole thing on each grid."

Shade in 0.25 on the transparent Decimal Grids A and B (T69–T70).

Show students a list of decimal numbers in tenths and hundredths and ask them to represent each of them on 10 × 10 Squares (M15). (Provide more copies as necessary.) Include one or two decimals that are greater than 1. For example:

0.35   0.8   0.49   1.5   2.75   0.15   0.05

Students shade in each decimal on one of the squares and compare their work with a partner's. They should write the number that they are representing under each square.

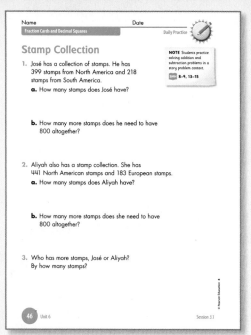

▲ Student Activity Book, p. 46

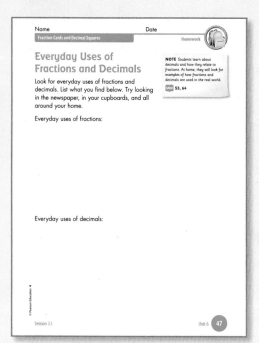

▲ Student Activity Book, p. 47

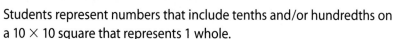

ONGOING ASSESSMENT: Observing Students at Work

Students represent numbers that include tenths and/or hundredths on a 10 × 10 square that represents 1 whole.

- **Can students represent the numbers on the 10 × 10 square?** Are there certain numbers that are more difficult?

- **Do students read and understand the meaning of the decimal numbers?** Can they say what the equivalent fractions are for these numbers? For example, do they know that 0.8 means $\frac{8}{10}$ and that 0.15 means $\frac{15}{100}$ or $\frac{1}{10} + \frac{5}{100}$?

As students work, ask questions such as these:

- How many tenths or hundredths are in this number?

- Is this number more or less than $\frac{1}{2}$? Is it more or less than 1?

- Can you write this number as a fraction? Does that help you think about what part of a whole it is?

make cards to match notation also with words

DIFFERENTIATION: Supporting the Range of Learners

Intervention Ask students who have difficulty representing both tenths and hundredths on the square to work only with tenths. Make sure that they can represent 0.1, 0.2, 0.3, and so on, before they work with 0.25, for example.

SESSION FOLLOW-UP

 Daily Practice and Homework

 Daily Practice: For ongoing review, have students complete *Student Activity Book* page 46.

 Homework: Students look in their home and in their neighborhood to find places where fractions and decimals are used. They record these on *Student Activity Book* page 47 and bring them back to school to add to the class list.

 Student Math Handbook: Students and families may use *Student Math Handbook* pages 64–68 for reference and review. See pages 170–176 in the back of this unit.

Comparing Decimals

Math Focus Points

◆ Reading and writing tenths and hundredths

◆ Representing tenths and hundredths as part of an area

◆ Ordering decimals and justifying their order through reasoning about representations and meaning of the numbers

Today's Plan		Materials
ACTIVITY **❶ Comparing 0.25 and 0.3**	20 MIN PAIRS CLASS	• M15 (as needed); T67
ACTIVITY **❷ Decimal Compare**	40 MIN PAIRS	• M27* (as needed); M15 (as needed); M26*; T71*
SESSION FOLLOW-UP **❸ Daily Practice and Homework**		• *Student Activity Book,* pp. 49–50 • *Student Math Handbook,* pp. 69; G4

*See *Materials to Prepare,* p. 101.

Ten-Minute Math

Practicing Place Value Write 0.2 on the board and have students practice saying it. Let students know that this number is commonly read both as "two tenths" and as "point 2." Make sure that all students can read, write, and say this number correctly.

What is one-tenth more than 0.2? What is 0.2 more? What is 0.5 more? What is 1 more?

Write each answer on the board. Ask students to compare each sum with 0.2. Which places have the same digits? Which do not? Why? If time remains, pose additional similar problems using these numbers: 0.6 and 0.7.

ACTIVITY

20 MIN   PAIRS   CLASS

Comparing 0.25 and 0.3

Distribute copies of 10 × 10 Squares (M15) to students.

Write 0.25 and 0.3 on the board.

Which of these two decimal fractions of the square is a larger portion of the square? How do you know? ❶

Ask students to use their 10 × 10 squares to illustrate their explanations. They should work with a partner and then be ready to share their thinking with the group. As students work, if you see some representations that you think will be useful for students to look at together, ask the students to copy those onto the transparency 10 × 10 Squares (T67).

Bring the class together to share a few responses. Some responses might be based on a drawing like the one below.

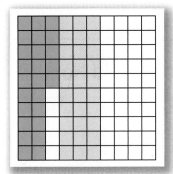

Students might say:

"I know that 0.25 is halfway between 0.2 and 0.3 (two tenths and three tenths) and 3 tenths is more than 2 and a half tenths."

"0.25 is the same as $\frac{25}{100}$, and 0.3 is the same as $\frac{30}{100}$. $\frac{30}{100}$ is more than $\frac{25}{100}$ because it is 30 pieces out of 100 instead of 25 pieces."

"0.25 is two and one half tenths. And 0.3 is 3 whole tenths, so it is $\frac{1}{2}$ of a tenth more."

"I thought 0.25 was bigger because it has more numbers in it. But when I drew the picture it was obvious that the 5 in the 0.25 is half of a tenth, so it is pretty small."

Write 0.5 and 0.45 on the board and ask students to determine which decimal is greater. Allow students to work for a few minutes and then bring them together to share their ideas.

Students might say:

 "I always look at the tenths first. I saw that 0.45 has $\frac{4}{10}$ and 0.5 has 5 tenths, so I knew that 0.5 is a larger number."

 "I got confused because 45 is a bigger number than 5. But then Amelia reminded me that the 4 in 0.45 and 5 in 0.5 are tenths and the 5 in 0.45 is 5 hundredths, which is really small compared to a tenth."

ONGOING ASSESSMENT: Observing Students at Work

Students compare decimal fractions of a 10 × 10 square.

- **Can students represent tenths and hundredths as part of the square?**

- **Can students use the representations and/or reason about the meaning of the decimal numbers to compare them?**

DIFFERENTIATION: Supporting the Range of Learners

(Intervention) If some students have difficulty comparing tenths and hundredths, they may need more time comparing decimals that are multiples of 0.1.

(Extension) Challenge students who can easily explain the given comparisons to compare 0.75 and 0.8 or 0.05 and 0.3. Ask them to determine not only which of the two is greater but how much greater it is.

(ELL) English Language Learners may have difficulty understanding the first question because of the complexity of its structure. A shorter series of questions with fewer prepositional phrases will enhance understanding. For example, say, 0.25 is a decimal fraction of this square. 0.3 is the decimal fraction of this square. Which is a larger part of the square? How do you know? Use models and write the questions on the board as needed.

Math Note

❶ **Place Value of Decimal Fractions** Many students apply their knowledge of whole numbers incorrectly to decimals. They may think that 0.25 is greater than 0.3 because they are thinking of the whole numbers 25 and 3. If no one brings up this issue, bring it up yourself. Why is 0.3 larger than 0.25 when 3 is so much smaller than 25? This allows students to explicitly think through the place value of the digits in these numbers in comparison to the value of the digits in 25 and 3.

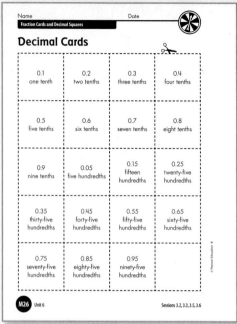

Decimal Cards

0.1 one tenth	0.2 two tenths	0.3 three tenths	0.4 four tenths
0.5 five tenths	0.6 six tenths	0.7 seven tenths	0.8 eight tenths
0.9 nine tenths	0.05 five hundredths	0.15 fifteen hundredths	0.25 twenty-five hundredths
0.35 thirty-five hundredths	0.45 forty-five hundredths	0.55 fifty-five hundredths	0.65 sixty-five hundredths
0.75 seventy-five hundredths	0.85 eighty-five hundredths	0.95 ninety-five hundredths	

M26 Unit 6   Sessions 3.2, 3.3, 3.5, 3.6

▲ Resource Masters, M26; T71

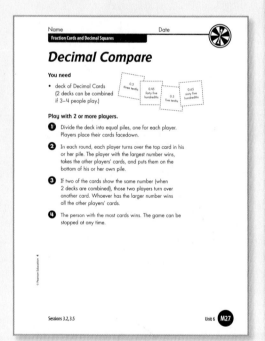

Decimal Compare

You need
- deck of Decimal Cards (2 decks can be combined if 3–4 people play.)

Play with 2 or more players.

❶ Divide the deck into equal piles, one for each player. Players place their cards facedown.

❷ In each round, each player turns over the top card in his or her pile. The player with the largest number wins, takes the other players' cards, and puts them on the bottom of his or her own pile.

❸ If two of the cards show the same number (when 2 decks are combined), those two players turn over another card. Whoever has the larger number wins all the other players' cards.

❹ The person with the most cards wins. The game can be stopped at any time.

Sessions 3.2, 3.5   Unit 6 M27

▲ Resource Masters, M27

ACTIVITY

② Decimal Compare

40 MIN   PAIRS

Students use their Decimal Cards (M26) to play *Decimal Compare.* They compare two decimal fractions that are multiples of 0.1 or of 0.05 and determine which is greater. Comparing these decimals provides an opportunity for students to become familiar with reading and writing decimals and determining the relative sizes of these numbers.

Introduce the game by writing two decimals from the deck of cards on the board or by showing two transparent Decimal Cards (T71) on the overhead. In this first example, choose two multiples of 0.1, such as 0.4 and 0.9, and ask students which is greater.

Although it should be fairly obvious to students that 0.9 is greater than 0.4, it is important to make sure that all students can read 0.9 as $\frac{9}{10}$ and be able to picture how much closer it is to 1 than $\frac{4}{10}$. Use a few more examples, including one or two in which students compare hundredths with hundredths and hundredths with tenths.

- How do you say this number?
- How do you know which number is larger?
- What does the digit in the tenths place mean? What does the digit in the hundredths place mean?
- Is this number more or less than 0.5? Is it more or less than 1?
- How many tenths more is the larger number?
- Can you show each of these numbers on a 10 × 10 square?

Students compare decimals on two Decimal Cards.

After examining a few examples for about ten minutes, explain to students that they will use their own set of Decimal Cards (M26) to play *Decimal Compare* with a partner. Although students have played several other types of "compare" games and will be familiar with the structure of the game, make available copies of the game rules *Decimal Compare* (M27).

ONGOING ASSESSMENT: Observing Students at Work

Students compare decimal numbers with digits in the tenths and/or hundredths places.

- **Can students read these numbers?**

- **Can students determine the value of each number?**

- **Can students determine which number is greater?** Do they have more difficulty with certain comparisons?

- **Do students visualize representing these numbers on the 10 × 10 square?** Do they reason about the relationship of the numbers to 1 or to 0.5?

DIFFERENTIATION: Supporting the Range of Learners

Intervention Some students may be able to visualize the numbers on a 10 × 10 square, but other students may need to actually represent each number in order to compare them. If students who need to shade in a grid for each number find that it takes too long to play each round, suggest a variation of the game: students pick a card, represent the number on a 10 × 10 Square (M15), and decide whether it is closer to $0, \frac{1}{2},$ or 1.

SESSION FOLLOW-UP

3 Daily Practice and Homework

Daily Practice: For ongoing review, have students complete *Student Activity Book* page 49.

Homework: On *Student Activity Book* page 50, students shade in the value of various decimals in tenths and hundredths on a 10 × 10 grid.

Student Math Handbook: Students and families may use *Student Math Handbook* pages 69 and G4 for reference and review. See pages 170–176 in the back of this unit.

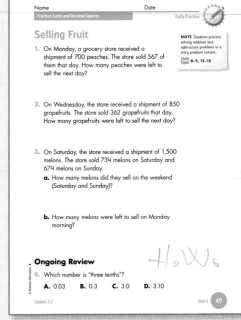

▲ Student Activity Book, p. 49

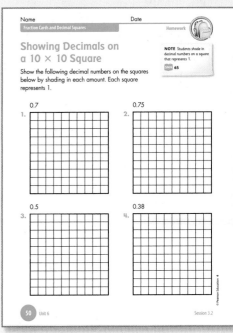

▲ Student Activity Book, p. 50

Representing and Combining Decimals

Math Focus Points

◆ Identifying decimal and fraction equivalents

◆ Representing tenths and hundredths as part of an area

◆ Using representations to combine tenths and hundredths

Today's Plan		Materials
① DISCUSSION $\frac{3}{10}$, 0.3, $\frac{30}{100}$	🕐 20 MIN 👥 CLASS 👥 PAIRS	• M15 (as needed); T67 🖨
② ACTIVITY *Playing Fill Two*	🕐 40 MIN 👥 CLASS 👥 PAIRS	• M28* (as needed); M15 (as needed); T67 🖨; M26 (from Session 3.2); T71 🖨 • Colored pencils, crayons, or markers (as needed)
③ SESSION FOLLOW-UP **Daily Practice**		• *Student Activity Book,* p. 51 • *Student Math Handbook,* pp. 69; G7

*See *Materials to Prepare,* p. 101.

Ten-Minute Math

Practicing Place Value Say "five tenths" and have students practice writing it. Let students know that this number is also commonly read as "point 5." Make sure all students can read, write, and say this number correctly.

What is 2 tenths more than this number? What is 0.02 more? What is 0.01 less?

Write each answer on the board. Ask students to compare each sum or difference with 0.5. Which places have the same digits? Which do not? Why? If time remains, pose additional similar problems using these numbers: 0.8 and 0.9.

MATH WORKSHOP

Comparing and Combining Decimals

60 MIN

Students continue to work on three activities to develop an understanding of how to compare and combine decimal numbers that include tenths and hundredths.

Observe students as they work and look for any confusions or misconceptions about the value of decimals or how they are combined. Bring students together for a short discussion about a specific problem if there is a need.

1A *Decimal Compare*

PAIRS

For complete details about this activity, see Session 3.2, page 114.

1B *Fill Two*

PAIRS

For complete details about this activity, see Session 3.3, pages 117–118.

1C *Making Your Own Running Logs*

INDIVIDUALS

For complete details about this activity, see Session 3.5, pages 129–130.

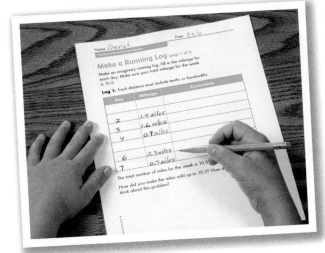

Students add decimals as they make their own Running Logs.

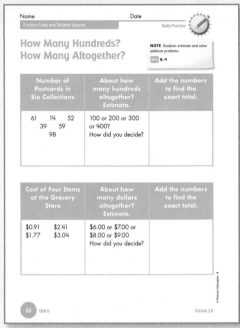

▲ Student Activity Book, p. 60

② Daily Practice

Daily Practice: For ongoing review, have students complete *Student Activity Book* page 60.

Student Math Handbook: Students and families may use *Student Math Handbook* pages 69–71 and G4, G7 for reference and review. See pages 170–176 in the back of this unit.

End-of-Unit Assessment

Math Focus Points

◆ Interpreting the meaning of the numerator and the denominator of a fraction

◆ Ordering fractions and justifying their order through reasoning about fraction equivalencies and relationships

◆ Ordering decimals and justifying their order through reasoning about representations and the meaning of the numbers

Today's Plan		Materials
① **ASSESSMENT ACTIVITY** **End-of-Unit Assessment**	✔ 🕐 👤 **60 MIN INDIVIDUALS**	• M31
② **SESSION FOLLOW-UP** **Daily Practice**		• *Student Activity Book,* p. 61 • *Student Math Handbook,* pp. 60–61, 69

*See *Materials to Prepare,* p. 103.

Ten-Minute Math

Practicing Place Value Write 1.2 on the board and have students practice saying it. Let students know that this number is commonly read both as "one and two tenths" and as "1 point 2." Make sure that all students can read, write, and say this number correctly. Ask:

• What is 0.4 more than this number? What is 0.05 more? 1 more? What is 0.3 less?

Write each answer on the board. Ask students to compare each sum or difference with 1.2. Which places have the same digits? Which do not? Why? If time remains, pose additional similar problems using these numbers: 1.8 and 2.1.

① Teacher Note: End-of-Unit Assessment, p. 159

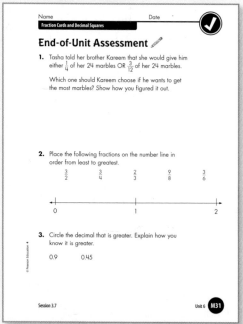

Name _____ Date _____ ✓

Fraction Cards and Decimal Squares

End-of-Unit Assessment ✏️

1. Tasha told her brother Kareem that she would give him either $\frac{1}{4}$ of her 24 marbles OR $\frac{3}{12}$ of her 24 marbles.

   Which one should Kareem choose if he wants to get the most marbles? Show how you figured it out.

2. Place the following fractions on the number line in order from least to greatest.

   $\frac{3}{2}$ $\frac{3}{4}$ $\frac{2}{3}$ $\frac{9}{8}$ $\frac{3}{6}$

   0   1   2

3. Circle the decimal that is greater. Explain how you know it is greater.

   0.9   0.45

Session 3.7   Unit 6 **M31**

▲ Resource Masters, M31

ASSESSMENT ACTIVITY
① End-of-Unit Assessment

60 MIN INDIVIDUALS

Students work individually on End-of-Unit Assessment (M31). The assessment has three problems. In Problem 1, students find one fourth and three twelfths of 24 marbles and decide which portion is greater. This addresses Benchmark 2: Identify fractional parts of a group (of objects, people, etc.), and Benchmark 4: Order fractions with like and unlike denominators. Benchmark 4 is also addressed by Problem 2, which asks students to order a set of five fractions along a number line. In Problem 3, students compare two decimal numbers; this addresses Benchmark 5: Read, write, and interpret decimal fractions in tenths and hundredths.①

Some students may complete the assessment in less than 60 minutes. These students can resume activities from the unit's Math Workshops, such as *Decimal Compare, Fill Two,* or *Capture Fractions.* After all students have finished, have a whole-group discussion sharing solutions to the assessment problems.

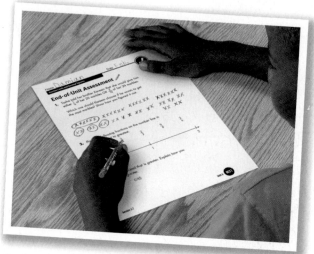

Students demonstrate how to find fractional parts of a group of objects in Problem 1 of the End-of-Unit Assessment.

DIFFERENTIATION: Supporting the Range of Learners

Intervention As students are working, check to make sure that they are communicating their thinking clearly so that you will be able to assess their work accurately. Ask any students whose work is not clear to explain their thinking to you, and help them show their work. Keep a record of any support you provided and any oral explanations students gave you.

Daily Practice

 Daily Practice: For enrichment, have students complete *Student Activity Book* page 61.

📖 **Student Math Handbook:** Student and families may use *Student Math Handbook* pages 60–61, 69 for reference and review. See pages 170–176 in the back of this unit.

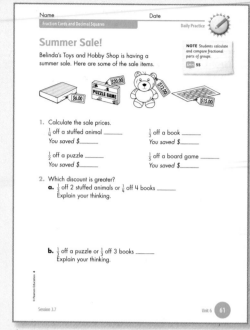

▲ **Student Activity Book, p. 61**

Fraction Cards and Decimal Squares

Teacher Notes

Why Are Fractions Difficult? Developing Meaning
for Fractions   139

Visualizing Fraction Equivalencies   141

Assessment: Identifying and Comparing Fractions   143

Keeping Track of the Whole   149

Strategies for Comparing Fractions   151

Assessment: Comparing Fractions   153

Extending Place Value to Tenths and Hundredths   157

End-of-Unit Assessment   159

In Part 6 of *Implementing Investigations in Grade 4,* you will find a
set of Teacher Notes that addresses topics and issues applicable
to the curriculum as a whole rather than to specific curriculum
units. They include the following:

Computational Fluency and Place Value

Computational Algorithms and Methods

Representations and Contexts for Mathematical Work

Foundations of Algebra in the Elementary Grades

Discussing Mathematical Ideas

Racial and Linguistic Diversity in the Classroom:
    What Does Equity Mean in Today's Math Classroom?

Dialogue Boxes

Finding Combinations That Equal 1   164

Comparing Fractions to Landmarks   165

Conjectures About Fractions   167

Are These Equal?   169

Student Math Handbook   170

Index   177

Why Are Fractions Difficult?
Developing Meaning for Fractions

Why are fractions difficult for elementary students? As adults, we are used to seeing fractions such as $\frac{1}{2}$ and $\frac{3}{4}$ in a variety of situations and ascribing meaning to them. It can be difficult for us to remember how strange these numbers may look to a fourth grader and what confusions may arise as students draw on their knowledge of whole numbers in an attempt to understand the meaning of fractions. There has been a great deal of research about students' understanding of fractions, largely with middle school students, that indicates that even in the middle grades, many students still interpret fraction notation as two separate whole numbers that are not related.

Imagine how two whole numbers separated by a line must look to elementary school children who are beginning to use fraction notation. It is not surprising that they try to draw on what they know from their extensive experience with the numbers with which they are most familiar—whole numbers. At first students might think that $\frac{1}{3}$ is greater than $\frac{1}{2}$ because 3 is greater than 2.

Looking at fractions as if they represent two separate whole numbers leads to misinterpretation of their meaning and an inability to assess the reasonableness of results of calculations with fractions. For example, in an oft-cited assessment question from the National Assessment of Educational Progress (NAEP), students were asked to pick an estimate for the sum of $\frac{12}{13}$ and $\frac{7}{8}$ from four choices: 1, 2, 19, and 21. Most students chose 19 or 21. Using whole number addition, they added either only the numerators or only the denominators. They were not able to think of each of these numbers as close to 1, so could not give a correct estimate of 2.

In order to develop meaning for fractions, students work with key ideas about fractions in the context of "fair shares" in which something is shared equally. In this unit, they divide rectangles into equal parts to represent fractions; they also draw their own representations to show equal

parts of a group of things. One key idea in this unit, and throughout students' study of fractions, is that a fraction represents a quantity in relation to a unit whole. This whole could be, for example, a single object, an area, a linear measure, or a group of objects. In this context, $\frac{1}{2}$ means 1 out of 2 equal parts that make up 1 whole.

One half of one whole is not the same quantity as one half of another whole; for example, $\frac{1}{2}$ of a class of 26 is 13 students, and $\frac{1}{2}$ of a class of 22 is 11 students. However, although $\frac{1}{2}$ can represent many different quantities, depending on the size of the whole, $\frac{1}{2}$ has the *same relationship* to *any* whole. It is 1 of the 2 equal parts that compose that quantity. In this unit, students work with fractions in relation to a whole that is a single object ($\frac{1}{4}$ of 1 sandwich), an area ($\frac{2}{3}$ of the area of a 4×6 rectangle), or a group of things ($\frac{1}{8}$ of the class). The focus is twofold: the parts of the whole must be equal to one another, and all the parts combined must equal the whole.

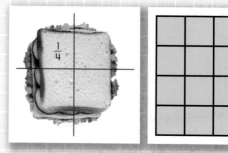

The ideas in this unit also lay the groundwork for division of a smaller number by a larger one. Just as students sometimes think, or are told by adults, "you can't subtract a larger number from a smaller one," when of course it is quite possible to solve such a problem when you know about negative numbers $(4 - 7 = -3)$, they may also think "you can't divide a smaller number by a larger one." Subtracting 7 from 4 requires expanding one's knowledge of the number system to include negative numbers. Similarly, dividing 3 by 4 requires expanding one's knowledge of the number system to include rational numbers (numbers that can be represented as a division of two integers, such as $\frac{1}{2}$ or $\frac{9}{10}$).

In fact, fractions indicate division: one interpretation of $\frac{1}{2}$ is that it represents one out of two equal parts of a whole, but it also means the quantity that results from dividing 1 by 2. In Grade 3, students were not yet thinking about fractions as an indicated division, but they learned about a fraction as a *relationship* between two numbers and how that relationship is, in turn, related to 1. In Grade 4 students focus more on how a fraction is a *number* that always has the same relationship to 1, extending their use of the number line with whole numbers to represent fractions, mixed numbers, and decimals as they order their Fraction Cards in Investigation 2 as shown below.

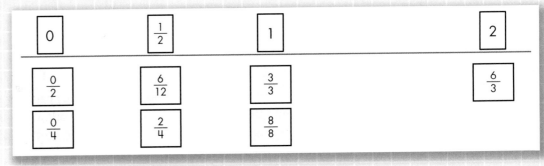

Visualizing Fraction Equivalencies

In this unit, students use area representations, pictures of groups, and number lines to build their knowledge of fraction equivalencies. They expand the work they did in Grade 3 with halves, fourths, eighths, thirds, and sixths and include other fractional parts, including fifths, tenths, and twelfths. Just as students build a repertoire of certain whole number equivalencies (e.g., the single-digit addition combinations or the different ways in which 138 might be decomposed), they also build a repertoire of fraction equivalencies.

One category of fraction equivalencies that students work on in this unit is individual fraction equivalents (e.g., $\frac{1}{2} = \frac{4}{8}$). They should bring with them knowledge of some of these equivalencies from Grade 3 and learn more in this unit. These include the following:

- The set of individual fractions that equal 1 ($\frac{2}{2}, \frac{3}{3}, \frac{6}{6}, \frac{4}{4}, \frac{8}{8}$)

- The set of fractions that equal $\frac{1}{2}$ ($\frac{2}{4}, \frac{3}{6}, \frac{4}{8}$)

- Pairs of fractions in which one fraction has a numerator and denominator that are double the numerator and denominator of the other ($\frac{1}{3} = \frac{2}{6}, \frac{1}{4} = \frac{2}{8}$, and $\frac{3}{4} = \frac{6}{8}$)

A second category of fraction equivalencies is addition combinations that are equivalent to 1 or to another fraction (e.g., $\frac{1}{2} + \frac{1}{4} + \frac{1}{4} = 1$, and $\frac{1}{3} + \frac{1}{6} = \frac{1}{2}$).

Throughout this unit, students use rectangles to help them develop visual images of how fractions or combinations of fractions are equivalent. They can see that two halves, three thirds, and six sixths make a whole.

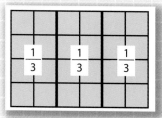

Similarly, students learn more equivalents for $\frac{1}{2}$. They should recognize that $\frac{2}{4}$ and $\frac{3}{6}$ are equivalent to $\frac{1}{2}$ from their work in Grade 3. In this unit, they also encounter $\frac{4}{8}$, $\frac{6}{12}$, and $\frac{5}{10}$. Students notice that these fractions (e.g., $\frac{2}{4}$, $\frac{3}{6}$, $\frac{4}{8}$, and so on) are characterized by a denominator that is twice the numerator. They notice that as the size of the fractional part is halved, the number of parts needed to make up the same quantity is doubled. In Grade 4, students encounter other fraction equivalents that have this characteristic, such as $\frac{2}{3}$ and $\frac{4}{6}$ or $\frac{3}{4}$ and $\frac{6}{8}$. In these cases, too, as the size of the fractional part is halved, the number of those parts is doubled to create an equivalent fraction.

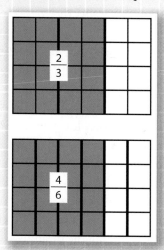

In the equal-sharing contexts of this unit, students often talk about this relationship as the size of the share being halved and the number of shares being doubled.

Students also use the areas of different rectangles to study addition of fractions. Students recognize that fractions with unlike denominators can be combined because they can draw and visualize these combinations. Without formally finding common denominators, they use their knowledge of fraction equivalencies to solve addition problems with unlike denominators and build a repertoire of known relationships.

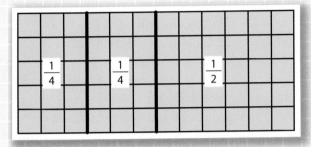

$$\frac{1}{4} + \frac{1}{4} + \frac{1}{2} = 1$$

In Grades 1–3, students worked on putting together and taking apart whole numbers. As they develop flexibility in decomposing numbers, they learn about the way our number system is structured and they develop computational methods based on this understanding. In Grades 3–5, students engage in developing this same kind of flexibility with fractions and decimal fractions. In Grade 4, students use fraction equivalencies they know to reason about other equivalencies, including combinations of fractions with sums greater than 1; for example, "Three sixths plus one half plus four eighths is 1 and a half, because three sixths is one half, and four eighths is one half, so that makes three halves. Two halves make one and then there's another half, so it's 1 and a half." Understanding the meaning of fractions and developing a repertoire of equivalencies are two of the key components that lay the groundwork for operations with fractions.

In Investigation 2, students compare and order fractions. The use of representations of fractions is still very important in this investigation, especially as students work more on representing mixed numbers and fractions greater than 1. They are still developing visual images of fractions and developing a repertoire of fraction equivalencies. However, students are also expected to reason about fraction comparisons on the basis of what they understand about the meaning of fractions, the relationship of a fraction to 1, and fraction equivalencies that they know. Although comparisons of some fractions, such as $\frac{1}{2}$ and $\frac{1}{4}$, are easy to make by using drawings of rectangles, many others are not. For example, drawings showing $\frac{1}{6}$ and $\frac{1}{5}$ may be slightly inaccurate, and it could easily appear that these two fractions are equivalent or even that $\frac{1}{6}$ is larger than $\frac{1}{5}$. At this point in their study of fractions, students should not be relying only on drawings to make fraction comparisons. For example, to compare $\frac{1}{6}$ and $\frac{1}{5}$, a student may get an idea from the drawings on the Fraction Cards but should be able to support that impression by reasoning about the relationship of $\frac{1}{5}$ and $\frac{1}{6}$—that $\frac{1}{5}$ represents one out of five equal parts and $\frac{1}{6}$ is one out of six equal parts of the same whole, so $\frac{1}{5}$ must be larger because it is one of fewer equal parts.

Assessment: Identifying and Comparing Fractions

Problem 1

Benchmarks addressed:

Benchmark 1: Identify fractional parts of an area.

Benchmark 3: Read, write, and interpret fraction notation.

In order to meet the benchmarks, students' work should show that they can:

- Identify the value of a fractional part of an area in relation to the whole;

- Explain how they know the value of the fractional part;

- Understand the meaning of the numerator and denominator of a fraction in the context of equal parts of a whole.

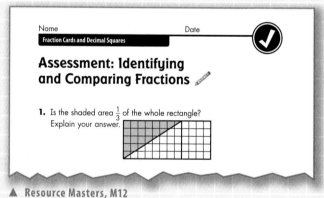

▲ **Resource Masters, M12**

Meeting the Benchmarks

Students who meet the benchmarks know that the shaded portion is $\frac{1}{3}$ of the whole rectangle and can explain how they know. They demonstrate an understanding that $\frac{1}{3}$ is one of 3 equal parts, usually by reasoning that there are 60 squares in the whole rectangle and that each of the parts contains 20 squares, which is $\frac{1}{3}$ of 60. A complete response to this problem also requires that students know that shapes that are not congruent can have an equal area. Further, they must draw on some of their knowledge about geometry, that a diagonal of a rectangle divides the rectangle into two equal parts, as Alejandro does.

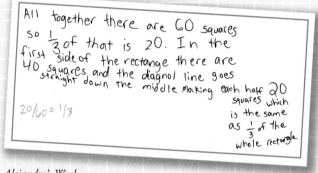

Alejandro's Work

Marisol also meets the benchmarks, although she is not explicit about how she knows that each triangular region contains 20 squares. Nevertheless, her reasoning about the problem in relation to these benchmarks is correct.

Marisol's Work

Ask students like Marisol how they know that there are 20 squares in each triangular region.

Partially Meeting the Benchmarks

Students who partially meet the benchmarks may know that an area of 20 squares equals one third of the whole rectangle but do not know how to determine whether there are 20 squares in the shaded portion. For example, Ursula attempts to count squares and pieces of squares.

> NO, Because
> If you
> count all
> the Boxes
> and add them they are all not even
>
> | 1 | 2 | 3 | 4 | 5 | 6 |
> | 7 | 8 | 9 | 10 |
> | 11 | 12 | 13 |
> | 14 |
>
> 20

Ursula's Work

Ursula's reasoning is correct: if the triangular region is *not* the same area as the 4 × 5 rectangular region, then the shaded part is not $\frac{1}{3}$ of the whole. However, she is not able to reason about the size of the triangular region.

Bill knows that identifying $\frac{1}{3}$ means finding one of three equal pieces, but he does not know how to determine whether the shaded area is equal to the other two. He says that you would have to "put in" two more of the triangles; that is, fit two more of the same triangular pieces with the shaded piece to make the whole. Bill may think that all of the pieces must be the same size and shape (that is, congruent) in order to have equal areas.

> No, because if it was then you would be able to put in two more of the same pieces. But you can't.

Bill's Work

These students can benefit by dividing rectangles into halves, thirds, and fourths that are different shapes (e.g., divide a 4 × 6 rectangle into fourths in such a way that none of the fourths are the same shape). They also need practice with finding equal areas by folding or cutting shapes to see whether they match. They can work with a simpler example of a rectangle divided into two parts by one of its diagonals in which it is still possible to count the squares easily (i.e., a 4 × 4 rectangle). They may first convince themselves that the two halves are equal by counting squares and half-squares. Then ask how they know that each part is half of the rectangle. "How can you tell without counting squares?" Encourage them to cut out the rectangles to see whether they match. Then try other rectangles for which it is not so easy to count the squares, such as the 4 × 6 Rectangle (M7).

Not Meeting the Benchmarks

Students who do not meet the benchmarks cannot identify a fractional part of an area. Some students may not know how $\frac{1}{3}$ is related to a whole, or some may give the wrong answer without any explanation.

A few students, such as Venetta, may give the correct answer but with an explanation that indicates lack of understanding of what $\frac{1}{3}$ is and its relationship to the whole.

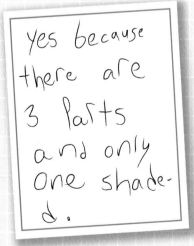

> yes because there are 3 parts and only one shaded.

Venetta's Work

Venetta explained that as long as there are three different parts, one of them is one third.

Venetta and other students need to continue working in the context of equal shares; for example, using the idea of dividing sandwiches from the beginning of this Investigation. What makes these equal? What fraction is each piece? Is each piece $\frac{1}{2}$ of the sandwich if the two pieces are unequal?

Problem 2

Benchmarks addressed:

Benchmark 2: Identify fractional parts of a group (of objects, people, etc.).

Benchmark 3: Read, write, and interpret fraction notation.

In order to meet the benchmarks, students' work should show that they can:

- Identify a fractional part of a group of objects;

- Explain how they know the value of the fractional part;

- Understand the meaning of the numerator and denominator of a fraction in the context of equal parts of a group.

> **2.** There are 24 apples in Mr. Lee's basket. $\frac{2}{6}$ of them spill out. How many did he lose? Explain how you know.

▲ **Resource Masters, M12**

Meeting the Benchmarks

Some students who meet the benchmarks find $\frac{1}{6}$ of 24, then double that because they know that $\frac{1}{6} + \frac{1}{6} = \frac{2}{6}$. Some students "just know" that $\frac{1}{6}$ of 24 is 4 and show that by dividing 24 by 6.

> Mr. Lee lost 8 apples, $\frac{1}{6}$ of 24 is 4. 4+4=8. So 8 apples, $\left(\frac{2}{6}\right)$ spilled out.

Luke's Work

> 8 apples, I know this because Mr. Lee lost 24÷6=4 and 4×2=8

Yuki's Work

Yuson represents the 24 apples in a 4 × 6 rectangular array—six rows with four apples in each row. She sees from her picture that one of the six groups contains four apples, so $\frac{1}{6}$ of 24 equals 4. Like Luke and Yuki, she doubles that amount to get $\frac{2}{6}$ of 24.

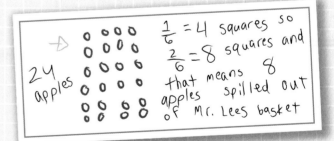

Yuson's Work

Jake uses knowledge of equivalent fractions. He knows that $\frac{2}{6} = \frac{1}{3}$ and finds $\frac{1}{3}$ of 24. He also shows that he knows that $\frac{1}{6}$ is half of $\frac{1}{3}$.

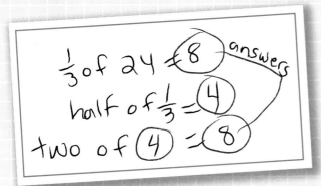

Jake's Work

Partially Meeting the Benchmarks

Some students may understand that they need to identify two groups out of six equal groups but make an error in computing the number of apples in the two groups. A few students find $\frac{1}{6}$ of 24 correctly, but then do not use that information to find $\frac{2}{6}$ of 24.

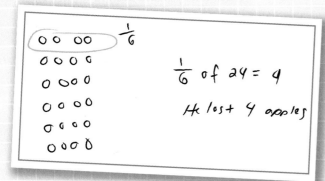

Kimberly's Work

Ask students like Kimberly to explain their work. Did she simply forget to complete the problem or does she have difficulty interpreting fractions with numbers other than 1 in the numerator?

Not Meeting the Benchmarks

Students who do not meet the benchmarks cannot identify a fractional part of a group of things. Many of these students are still grappling with the meaning of fractions and how fractions represent quantities. They often draw on their experience with whole numbers. For example, both Richard and Steve appear to be thinking about groups of six objects rather than $\frac{1}{6}$ of the objects:

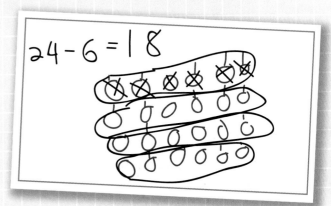

Richard's Work

He has 12 left because if you think of 2×6 = 12 and 12×12 = 24 that is how I got my answer

Steve's Work

Richard makes groups of six then subtracts one of those groups from 24, as if he is thinking about "1 group of 6" rather than one out of six equal groups. Similarly, Steve finds the value of two groups of six, and then subtracts that result from 24, getting an incorrect answer of 12.

Because students usually have developed meaning for $\frac{1}{2}$ of a group of things, these students can benefit from working on problems like those on *Student Activity Book* page 12, starting with unit fractions: $\frac{1}{2}$ and $\frac{1}{4}$, and then $\frac{1}{3}$ and $\frac{1}{6}$. Ask these students to explain how they know what $\frac{1}{2}$ of a class of 24 students is, and then build on their own explanations to help them work with $\frac{1}{4}$ and $\frac{1}{3}$ of a group.

Helena knows that $\frac{1}{6} + \frac{1}{6} = \frac{2}{6}$, but she incorrectly identifies $\frac{1}{6}$ of 24 as 2. Because she does not explain how she found each sixth, it is impossible to determine how she arrived at her result.

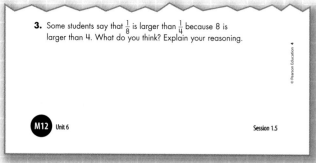

Helena's Work

Helena seems to understand that $\frac{2}{6}$ is two of six equal parts of the group of objects. She may have made a computation error or she may be confused about how to divide a group of 24 into six equal parts. Ask students like Helena to explain their work more fully to determine what they do not understand.

Problem 3

Benchmarks addressed:

Benchmark 3: Read, write, and interpret fraction notation.

Benchmark 4: Order fractions with like and unlike denominators.

In order to meet the benchmarks, students' work should show that they can:

• Explain or demonstrate the meaning of the numerator and denominator of a fraction.

---

3. Some students say that $\frac{1}{8}$ is larger than $\frac{1}{4}$ because 8 is larger than 4. What do you think? Explain your reasoning.

© Pearson Education 4

M12 Unit 6   Session 1.5

▲ **Resource Masters, M12**

Meeting the Benchmarks

This problem often elicits strong responses from students who are eager to "prove" the correct answer to the imaginary students in the problem. Students who meet the benchmark can use a representation or reason about the meaning of fractions to show that $\frac{1}{8}$ is a smaller quantity than $\frac{1}{4}$ when compared to the same whole.

Anna enthusiastically and articulately explains in words and with a representation that $\frac{1}{4}$ is larger because $\frac{1}{4}$ is one of four equal parts, whereas $\frac{1}{8}$ is one of eight equal parts. She relates this to a practical situation of dividing a pizza into slices: dividing it equally among eight people results in smaller slices than dividing it equally among four people. This can be easily seen in her drawings of circles because each circle is approximately the same size and $\frac{1}{8}$ is clearly smaller than $\frac{1}{4}$.

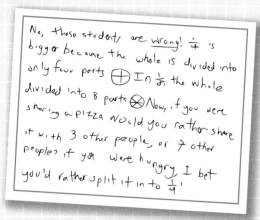

Anna's Work

Damian also uses a representation to clearly compare $\frac{1}{8}$ and $\frac{1}{4}$. His two rectangles are (approximately) equal in size, and he not only shows that $\frac{1}{8}$ is a smaller part of the whole than $\frac{1}{4}$ but also shows the relationship between the two fractions by splitting each fourth into two eighths. Damian includes a general statement about fractions: " . . . the larger the number gets the smaller the parts get." Although he does not specify that "the number" is the denominator, it is clear that he is stating a general rule about the relative size of unit fractions with different denominators.

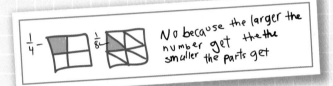

Damian's Work

Sabrina uses only words to highlight an important relationship between $\frac{1}{4}$ and $\frac{1}{8}$. She notes that $\frac{1}{8}$ is half of $\frac{1}{4}$, so, of course, $\frac{1}{8}$ is smaller.

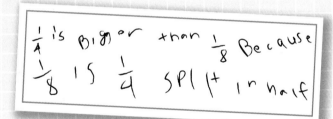

Sabrina's Work

Partially Meeting the Benchmarks

Students who partially meet the benchmark may correctly identify $\frac{1}{4}$ as more than $\frac{1}{8}$ but provide an incomplete explanation. Ask students to write more or to talk through their ideas with you to see whether they have a clear understanding of the relationship between $\frac{1}{4}$ and $\frac{1}{8}$.

Not Meeting the Benchmarks

Students who do not meet the benchmark either correctly identify $\frac{1}{4}$ as the greater fraction but do not provide an explanation or incorrectly identify $\frac{1}{8}$ as the greater fraction.

For example, Richard simply asserts that $\frac{1}{4}$ is bigger, but provides no explanation.

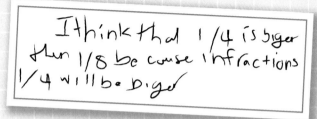

Richard's Work

Richard could be asked, "How do you know that $\frac{1}{4}$ is bigger? Can you show me so that I am convinced?" He should be encouraged to use a representation, such as two rectangular 4×6 grids, to compare the two fractions.

Bill uses two wholes to show $\frac{1}{8}$ and compares that to one whole on which he has shown $\frac{1}{4}$, while other students do not show how to represent the fractions at all.

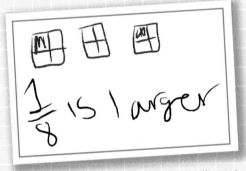

Bill's Work

These students are still having difficulty with understanding the most basic ideas about fractions—that they represent equal parts of a whole. See **Teacher Note:** Why Are Fractions Difficult? Developing Meaning for Fractions, page 139, for some background that may be helpful as you think about these students. It is important to find out what students like Bill and Cheyenne do know and understand about fractions. Can they find $\frac{1}{2}$, $\frac{1}{4}$, and $\frac{1}{8}$ of a rectangle and explain how they know the value of each fractional part?

Keeping Track of the Whole

As students work with fractions that are greater than 1, many fourth graders have to rethink how the fractional part is related to the whole. When students work with fractions less than 1, such as $\frac{1}{2}$ or $\frac{2}{3}$, they think about splitting the whole into the number of equal parts indicated by the denominator. The numerator then tells them how many of those equal parts are represented by the fraction. In Grades 3 and 4, students have represented equal shares in the context of rectangular shapes (sometimes brownies or sandwiches) and in the context of groups of things.

Now as they work with fractions such as $\frac{3}{2}$ or $\frac{7}{4}$, they have to expand the way they visualize fractions to include the possibility of more than one whole. At first, many students struggle with this idea. For example, Ramona drew $\frac{4}{3}$ like this:

Ramona's Work

She said, "I stuck two pieces together." She had first drawn one rectangle and divided it into three thirds. Then, because she needed one more third, she drew another rectangle with three thirds connected to the first and shaded in one more third. She was stumped by the need to have four pieces shaded when thirds only provide three in a single whole. In some ways, her solution is correct, if she is still thinking of her picture as representing two wholes. However, if she is seeing the new rectangle as her whole, she has shown $\frac{4}{6}$ instead of $\frac{4}{3}$.

Derek provides another example. He had been representing fractions less than 1 easily in Investigation 1, but in Investigation 2, he became confused about representing fractions greater than 1. For a while, he also seemed to lose his grasp of fractions less than 1. For example, he made this picture for $\frac{1}{5}$:

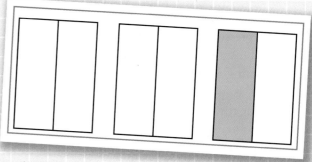

Derek's Work

As he started to need more than one whole to represent some fractions, such as $\frac{8}{6}$ and $\frac{9}{4}$, on his Fraction Cards, he began to make more than one whole even when it was not needed.

Both Ramona and Derek can benefit from going back to some of their work in Investigation 1, such as representing $\frac{1}{3}$, then $\frac{2}{3}$, and then $\frac{3}{3}$ of a 4 × 6 or 5 × 12 rectangle. Using contexts to talk through fractional parts can also be very helpful.

You're saying that $\frac{3}{3}$ means all of one whole sandwich, so if you eat $\frac{3}{3}$ of a sandwich, you eat the whole thing. You also said that if you ate $\frac{2}{3}$ of the sandwich, you would not eat the whole sandwich; you'd eat only two of the three equal parts. So what could it mean to eat $\frac{4}{3}$ of a sandwich? Would that be more or less than $\frac{3}{3}$ of a sandwich?

Another issue in representing fractions or mixed numbers greater than 1 is illustrated by Abdul's work. He represented $\frac{4}{3}$ like this:

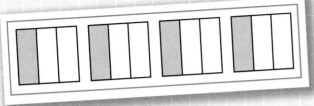

Abdul's Work

Instead of representing $\frac{4}{3}$ as one rectangle with three thirds and a second rectangle with one third, he shows four rectangles with $\frac{1}{3}$ shaded in each. He may have been thinking of $\frac{4}{3}$ as four things (such as sandwiches) divided equally among three people. One easy way of making these equal shares is to divide each of the four sandwiches into three equal parts; then each person gets one of the thirds from each sandwich. Each person's share is $\frac{4}{3}$ of a sandwich.

This way of representing $\frac{4}{3}$ is a very good representation of the meaning of a fraction as division: four wholes divided equally into three shares. It also models how $\frac{4}{3}$ is composed: $\frac{4}{3} = \frac{1}{3} + \frac{1}{3} + \frac{1}{3} + \frac{1}{3}$. However, students like Abdul who visualize $\frac{4}{3}$ in this way sometimes have difficulty understanding how this picture can also represent $\frac{4}{3}$ and may not have a clear idea that his $\frac{4}{3}$ is $\frac{4}{3}$ of *one sandwich*.

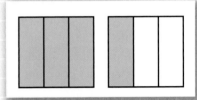

It can be very fruitful for all students to compare these two pictures. How are they similar? How are they different? If the sandwiches in Abdul's picture were cut into thirds and those thirds were rearranged, could his $\frac{4}{3}$ match the $\frac{4}{3}$ in the picture of two sandwiches? Is $\frac{4}{3}$ of a sandwich more than one sandwich? More than two sandwiches? What about $\frac{6}{3}$ of a sandwich? What about $\frac{7}{3}$ of a sandwich? If you eat nine of the $\frac{1}{3}$ pieces, that would be equivalent to how many sandwiches?

Strategies for Comparing Fractions

Listen to students comparing fractions as they play *Capture Fractions* and order fractions during Investigation 2. Students develop a number of strategies that work for certain kinds of comparisons. You can help students become more explicit about the underlying regularities they are noticing as they use these strategies by asking questions such as these:

What types of fractions does your strategy work for? Can you give me another example of a comparison of two fractions when this strategy would work?

Bring these ideas to the attention of the whole class, and ask students when a strategy works and why. Start a list of conjectures that are based on what students are noticing.

Can you come up with a rule about your strategy—how it works and what kinds of fractions it works for?

Here are some examples, expressed in students' words, of strategies they develop and conjectures they might articulate, given the general ideas underlying each strategy.

Comparing Fractions with the Same Denominator

Example: $\frac{3}{12}$ and $\frac{2}{12}$

"All the pieces are the same size. So if you have three, of course it's more than two."

Conjecture: When the denominators are the same, the fraction with the larger numerator is larger.

Comparing Fractions with the Same Numerator

Example: $\frac{3}{8}$ and $\frac{3}{4}$

"Three eighths is less than three fourths because four parts is less than eight, so the fourths are bigger than the eighths. So if you have the same number of parts, but the fourths are bigger, then three fourths has to be bigger."

Conjecture: When the numerators are the same, the fraction with the smaller denominator is larger.

Fractions in Which the Numerator and Denominator of One Fraction Are Double Those of the Other

Example: $\frac{4}{10}$ and $\frac{2}{5}$

"In my rectangle, you can see that this shaded part is four tenths, but if you just make them into fifths, you have to use two of the tenths for a fifth, so you cut the number of pieces in half, and you cut the denominator in half because now there are only five pieces, not ten."

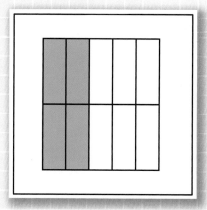

Conjecture: If the numerator and denominator of one fraction (such as $\frac{4}{10}$) are double the numerator and denominator of another fraction (such as $\frac{2}{5}$), the two fractions are equivalent.

Comparing Fractions to 1

Example: $\frac{4}{5}$ and $\frac{4}{3}$

"There is one whole in four thirds with some still left over, and four fifths isn't even one."

Conjecture: If a fraction has a numerator that is less than the denominator (such as $\frac{4}{5}$), it is less than one. If a fraction has a numerator that is more than the denominator (such as $\frac{4}{3}$), it is greater than one.

Example: $\frac{4}{5}$ and $\frac{7}{8}$

"Seven eighths is only one eighth away from one. But four fifths is one fifth away from one. An eighth is smaller than a fifth, and so seven eighths is just a little smidge from one. Seven eighths is closer to one, so it's bigger."

Conjecture: If two fractions are just one piece less than one, the fraction with smaller pieces is bigger.

Comparing Fractions to $\frac{1}{2}$

Example: $\frac{2}{5}$ and $\frac{1}{2}$

"If there are five pieces in the rectangle, one half the rectangle has two and a half pieces. One half has two and a half fifths, so two fifths is smaller because it only has two fifths."

Conjecture: If the numerator of a fraction is less than half the denominator, the fraction is less than $\frac{1}{2}$.

Example: $\frac{2}{5}$ and $\frac{3}{8}$

"For three eighths, you need another one eighth to make one half. For two fifths, you need half of a fifth to make one half. That's the same as one tenth. One tenth is smaller than one eighth, so two fifths is closer to one half. That means that two fifths is more."

Conjecture: If you have two fractions that are less than $\frac{1}{2}$ and you look at the missing piece to get to $\frac{1}{2}$, the fraction with the smallest missing piece is larger than the other one.

Assessment: Comparing Fractions

Benchmarks addressed:

Benchmark 3: Read, write, and interpret fraction notation.

Benchmark 4: Order fractions with like and unlike denominators.

In order to meet the benchmarks, students' work should show that they can:

- Understand the meaning of the numerator and denominator of each fraction;

- Interpret the value of each fraction as a number (for example, in relation to a landmark such as $\frac{1}{2}$ or 1);

- Determine and demonstrate which fraction is greater by using explanations based on knowledge of fraction equivalencies and relationships.

When students compare each of these pairs of fractions they provide evidence of important understandings about the relationships of fractions to one another and to 1, including:

- whether students draw on knowledge of equivalent fractions.

- whether students recognize when a fraction is less than or more than $\frac{1}{2}$.

- whether students can interpret the meaning of the numerator and denominator of a fraction in order to determine whether it is greater than or less than 1.

- whether students can determine the difference between a fraction and 1.

Based on this assessment, you can determine whether some of your students need more time to work on any of these important ideas about fractions.

Problem 1

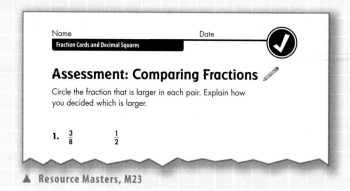

▲ **Resource Masters, M23**

Meeting the Benchmarks

Students who meet the benchmarks demonstrate that they know $\frac{3}{8}$ is less than $\frac{1}{2}$ and can explain how they know. Most students explain that $\frac{3}{8}$ is $\frac{1}{8}$ less than $\frac{4}{8}$, which is equivalent to $\frac{1}{2}$. Therefore, $\frac{3}{8}$ is less than $\frac{1}{2}$.

Anna draws two rectangles that are approximately the same size, shows $\frac{1}{2}$ on one, and shows $\frac{1}{2}$ that is missing $\frac{1}{8}$ on the other. She explains that the $\frac{3}{8}$ is "missing one part"— that is, it would need an additional eighth to be equivalent to $\frac{1}{2}$.

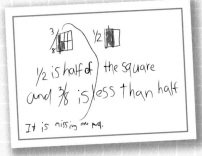

Anna's Work

Barney uses the same reasoning but does not use a model.

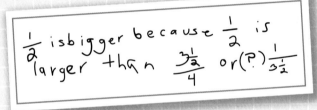

$\frac{3}{8}$ is $\frac{1}{8}$ away from $\frac{1}{2}$ that is why $\frac{1}{2}$ is larger.

Barney's Work

Another student articulates the relationship between the numerator and denominator by writing the following: "$\frac{3}{8}$ is less than $\frac{1}{2}$ because half of eight is four and there are only $\frac{3}{8}$. And if it were $\frac{5}{8}$, it would be $\frac{1}{8}$ *more* than $\frac{1}{2}$."

Partially Meeting the Benchmarks

Some students may draw a picture that shows that $\frac{3}{8}$ *looks like* less than $\frac{1}{2}$ but may provide no explanation. The drawings may be quite accurate, but it is important that students include their reasoning because in other cases a drawing will not be accurate enough to determine relative size.

Thus, Cheyenne does not fully meet the benchmark even though her drawing shows that $\frac{3}{8}$ is $\frac{1}{8}$ less than $\frac{1}{2}$. Cheyenne has drawn a picture of each fraction, but she does not explain her reasoning.

Cheyenne's Work

Ask students like Cheyenne to explain their ideas further. Can she make use of equivalent fractions such as $\frac{1}{2} = \frac{4}{8}$? Can she describe how $\frac{3}{8}$ is $\frac{1}{8}$ less than $\frac{1}{2}$?

Not Meeting the Benchmarks

Some students may demonstrate a lack of understanding of the meaning of the two fractions or may draw an incorrect representation.

In some cases, students may correctly identify the greater fraction but their explanation reveals confusion about how to compare the two fractions. For example, Derek tries to find a way to compare $\frac{1}{2}$ and $\frac{3}{8}$ by thinking about related fractions. He knows that $\frac{1}{2} = \frac{2}{4}$. He tries to figure out how many fourths are equal to $\frac{3}{8}$. He incorrectly determines that $3\frac{1}{2}$ fourths is equal to $\frac{3}{8}$. And it is unclear what he is thinking when he writes 1 over $3\frac{1}{2}$. It is important to find out whether Derek can model $\frac{3}{8}$ and $\frac{1}{2}$ on rectangles and whether he can figure out how many eighths there are in $\frac{1}{2}$.

$\frac{1}{2}$ is bigger because $\frac{1}{2}$ is larger than $\frac{3\frac{1}{2}}{4}$ or(?)$\frac{1}{3\frac{1}{2}}$

Derek's Work

Problem 2

2. $\frac{2}{3}$ $\frac{5}{6}$

▲ **Resource Masters, M23**

Meeting the Benchmarks

This pair of fractions can highlight a misconception among students that fractions that have "one piece missing" are equal; that is, some students mistakenly reason that because $\frac{3}{3}$, $\frac{4}{4}$, $\frac{5}{5}$, $\frac{6}{6}$, and so on are all equivalent to one whole, then fractions that are $\frac{1}{3}$ or $\frac{1}{4}$ or $\frac{1}{5}$ or $\frac{1}{6}$ less than 1 are all equal. These fractions, like $\frac{2}{3}$, $\frac{3}{4}$, $\frac{4}{5}$, and $\frac{5}{6}$, all have "one piece missing" to make a whole.

Students who meet the benchmark can figure out that $\frac{5}{6}$ is larger than $\frac{2}{3}$ and explain how they know. Most students use one as a benchmark. They reason that each fraction is one piece away from one whole, but the piece missing from $\frac{5}{6}$ ($\frac{1}{6}$) is smaller than the piece missing from $\frac{2}{3}$ ($\frac{1}{3}$) so $\frac{5}{6}$ is *closer* to one and therefore larger.

In this example, Jill compares two rectangles and explains that the $\frac{1}{6}$ piece—"what is left over"—is smaller than the $\frac{1}{3}$ piece.

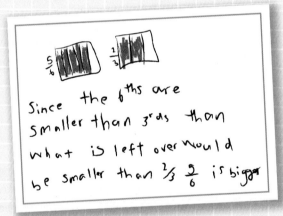

Jill's Work

Another student, Steve, explains that $\frac{1}{6}$ is smaller than $\frac{1}{3}$, so "more is needed" to be added to $\frac{2}{3}$, which makes $\frac{5}{6}$ closer to one.

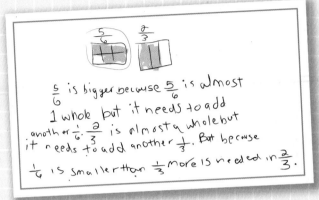

Steve's Work

Andrew uses knowledge of equivalent fractions to compare $\frac{2}{3}$ and $\frac{5}{6}$. He knows that $\frac{2}{3}$ is equal to $\frac{4}{6}$. So $\frac{5}{6}$ is $\frac{1}{6}$ larger than $\frac{2}{3}$. His illustration shows how $\frac{5}{6}$ has one more sixth than $\frac{2}{3}$.

Andrew's Work

Partially Meeting the Benchmarks

As in Problem 1, some students may draw a picture of each fraction and identify which is larger but provide no explanation. The explanation is critical in determining what students understand about fractions.

Not Meeting the Benchmarks

Some students may demonstrate a lack of understanding of the meaning of the two fractions or may draw an incorrect representation. In this comparison, students who rely only on representations can easily conclude that the two fractions are equal or that $\frac{2}{3}$ is more than $\frac{5}{6}$.

Some students may demonstrate confusion about each fraction missing one piece and think they are equal: "$\frac{5}{6}$ and $\frac{2}{3}$ are the same amount because each has one remainder, so I think they are the same."

Some students may provide explanations that do not express knowledge about fraction equivalents or relationships and need to be questioned further to see what they do and do not understand about fractions. For example, one student wrote, "I think they are equal because you just switched the numbers." Other students may still be relying on their knowledge of whole numbers "3 and 6 are related and 2 and 5 are related in the same way." This student might be considering the difference between 5 and 2 and the difference between 6 and 3.

Problem 3

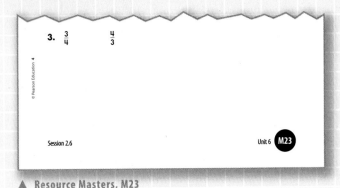

▲ Resource Masters, M23

Meeting the Benchmarks

This pair of fractions highlights the meaning of the numerator and denominator and assesses whether students can identify a fraction that is greater than 1.

Students who meet the benchmark usually relate the two fractions to one. It is important that students do not simply assert that $\frac{3}{4}$ is less than one and $\frac{4}{3}$ is more than one, but that they can represent or explain why this is true. For example, Abdul explains that $\frac{4}{3}$ is equivalent to $1\frac{1}{3}$.

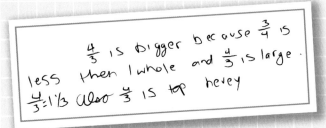

Abdul's Work

Partially Meeting the Benchmarks

As in Problems 1 and 2, some students may draw a picture of each fraction and identify which is larger but provide no explanation.

Not Meeting the Benchmarks

Some students may be able to show $\frac{3}{4}$ on a rectangle but may also show $\frac{4}{3}$ in the same way, as three out of four equal parts. They have not yet sorted out the meaning of a fraction in which the numerator is more than the denominator.

Students who can solve only Problem 1 or who have difficulty with all three of the problems on this assessment should do more work with representing fractions on the 4×6 and 5×12 rectangles. Students who have trouble with either Problems 2 or 3 can benefit from spending more time playing *Capture Fractions* and can continue using their Fraction Cards to order subsets of the cards on the number line. You can choose a subset of the cards that contains many fractions with which they are familiar and a few of the fractions that are difficult for them.

Extending Place Value to Tenths and Hundredths

Students have spent a great deal of time in elementary school working with the place value of whole numbers. In this unit, students focus on extending their understanding of the place-value system to tenths and hundredths.

The base-ten number system (also called the *decimal number system*) is a *place-value* system; that is, any numeral, such as 2, can represent different values, depending on where it appears in a written number: it can represent 2 ones, 2 tens, 2 hundreds, 2 thousands, and so on. Understanding a place-value system requires coordinating the way we write the numerals that represent a particular number (e.g., 5,217) and the way we name numbers in words (e.g., five thousand, two hundred seventeen) with how those symbols represent quantities. (See **Part 6: Teacher Notes** in *Investigations* in *Implementing Investigations in Grade 4:* Computational Fluency and Place Value.)

Numbers that include amounts less than one are represented as a continuation of the base-ten system with numerals to the right of the decimal point. The decimal point separates the integer and fractional parts of the number. The structure of the place-value system continues to hold true for these digits to the right of the decimal point. A digit in any place represents a value ten times greater than the same digit in the place immediately to the right and one-tenth of the value of the same digit in the place immediately to the left:

222.22
two hundred twenty-two and twenty-two hundredths

From left to right, the digits represent 2 hundreds, 2 tens, 2 ones, 2 tenths, and 2 hundredths. The digit in the hundreds place represents a quantity ten times greater than the digit in the tens place. The digit in the tenths place represents a quantity ten times greater than the digit in the hundredths place.

×10	×10	×10	×10	×10	×10
thousands	hundreds	tens ones	tenths	hundredths	thousandths
÷10	÷10	÷10	÷10	÷10	÷10

One of the problems for students in understanding decimals is that the amounts represented by tenths, and even more so by hundredths, are very small. They are much more experienced with whole numbers in their lives. Just as very large numbers are difficult to visualize, so are very small numbers. Students do not generally deal with hundredths in their everyday experience or, when they do, it is difficult to actually perceive the magnitude of those numbers. For example, 0.1 second and 0.01 second both represent a very short amount of time—the difference between them is not perceptible without specialized tools. It is perhaps easier to distinguish between 0.1 mile and 0.01 mile, but these are not quantities that come up in students' everyday experience. Smaller amounts—0.001 second or mile—are even more difficult to imagine. Yet understanding that 0.1 is ten times bigger than 0.01 is crucial to understanding and computing with decimals.

This same relationship holds true for whole numbers, such as 50 and 5 (50 is 10 times bigger than 5, 5 is one tenth of 50), but both the change in magnitude and the actual size of the numbers are more obvious in real situations: there is a noticeable difference between 50 seconds and 5 seconds. Even though the structure of the place-value system is the same for digits that indicate the fractional part of the number, experience in classrooms is that students need time to develop an understanding of the quantity, order, and equivalence with regard to these very small numbers.

The decimal point is the conventional separator used in the United States to separate the integer part of a number from parts of the number that are less than 1. One of the first understandings students should be developing is that digits to the right of the decimal point indicate that the quantity is greater than the whole-number portion of the number and less than the next largest whole number. For example, consider a swimmer who swims the 100-meter freestyle in 51.34 seconds. The part of the number represented by "0.34" indicates a fractional amount: it took more than 51 seconds for the swimmer to complete the race, but less than 52 seconds.

Learning about numbers that include digits to the right of the decimal point is further complicated by the way we read the numbers. The decimal portion of the number above is conventionally read as "twenty-two hundredths" rather than "two tenths and two hundredths." Students may at first read numbers in this second way, which actually indicates their understanding of the place value of each digit. Gradually students learn that two tenths plus two hundredths is equivalent to twenty-two hundredths and that the number is read in this way. This number is also conventionally read as "two hundred twenty-two point twenty-two," and students should also hear numbers read in this way so that they will recognize this way of reading decimals.

The use of zeroes in decimal notation can be confusing to students. Students should sometimes see decimal numbers that are less than 1 written with a zero in the ones place, for example, 0.5. Including the zero helps to remind students that the decimal point separates the whole number portion of the number (which, in this case, is zero) from the part that is less than 1. However, students should also see numbers such as .5 written without the zero in the ones place, so that they recognize that 0.5 = .5.

Students also learn about zeroes in places to the right of nonzero digits, such as 0.5 = 0.50. Students are learning that five tenths (0.5) and fifty hundredths (0.50) are equal amounts. (Note that mathematically 0.5 and 0.50 are the same number; however, in statistics, science, and engineering, writing 0.5 or 0.50 may suggest a different level of confidence in the accuracy of results.)

In this unit, squares divided into tenths, hundredths, and thousandths are used as representations to help students visualize the relationship of these small numbers to one another and to 1. Students have been using representations similar to these to understand large numbers (for example, the 10,000 chart they use in Unit 5, *Landmarks and Large Numbers*). Now, instead of building up a hundred, then a thousand, then 10,000, from single square units, they start with a single square unit and break it into smaller and smaller parts. What is critical is that students think of this square unit as one whole and the divisions of the square as equal parts of that one whole.

End-of-Unit Assessment

Problem 1

Benchmarks addressed:

Benchmark 2: Identify fractional parts of a group (of objects, people, etc.).

Benchmark 4: Order fractions with like and unlike denominators.

In order to meet the benchmarks, students' work should show that they can:

- Compare these quantities either by finding the fractions of 24 or by reasoning about the equivalence of $\frac{1}{4}$ and $\frac{3}{12}$.

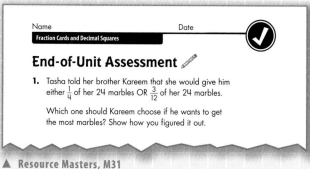

▲ **Resource Masters, M31**

Meeting the Benchmarks

Students who meet the benchmarks can show clearly that $\frac{1}{4}$ of 24 is equal to $\frac{3}{12}$ of 24 using representations or by reasoning about the meaning of the fractions. The following examples demonstrate three different ways students might explain that the two quantities are equal.

Emaan shows two sets of 24 objects. He divides the first set into four equal groups and identifies one of these groups of 6 as $\frac{1}{4}$. On the other set, he identifies $\frac{1}{12}$ of the groups as 2 marbles. He sees that these two quantities are equal and records $\frac{1}{4} = \frac{3}{12}$.

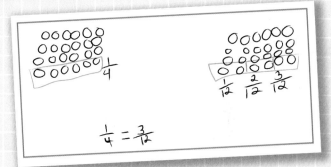

Emaan's Work

Another student, Tonya, uses her knowledge that $6 \times 4 = 24$ to figure out that $\frac{1}{4}$ of 24 is 6. She also knows that 12 groups of 2 equal 24, so three of those groups of 2 is $\frac{3}{12}$ of the marbles.

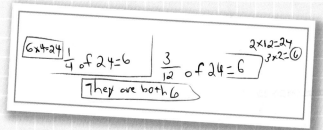

Tonya's Work

Venetta shows $\frac{1}{4}$ and $\frac{3}{12}$ on the same 4×6 rectangle. This is one of the representations used in the unit, and she seems to have chosen wisely because it easily accommodates both fourths and twelfths. She identifies $\frac{1}{12}$ as 2 squares, and three of those are shaded in as $\frac{3}{12}$. It is clear from her drawing that the two fractions are equal.

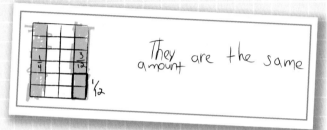

Venetta's Work

Partially Meeting the Benchmarks

Some students may have the correct answer to the problem but may offer no explanation or representation that shows their reasoning. In this case, it is impossible to determine how much they understand about fractions and whether they can extend their understanding to other problems. If a student's answer is limited to "It doesn't matter, they are the same thing," ask questions such as these:

How do you know that they are equal? How can you compare fourths and twelfths? Can you show me $\frac{1}{4}$ and $\frac{3}{12}$? What does the denominator mean? The numerator?

Other students show knowledge about fourths and twelfths but are not able to solve the problem. For example, Yuki demonstrates an understanding of fractions as equal pieces of a whole but compares $\frac{1}{12}$ and $\frac{1}{4}$ of the marbles instead of $\frac{3}{12}$ and $\frac{1}{4}$. Ask questions to find out whether a student like Yuki simply did not keep in mind all parts of the problem or had difficulty with the meaning of fractions with numerators greater than one.

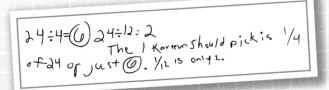

Yuki's Work

Not Meeting the Benchmarks

Students who do not meet the benchmarks show confusion about the meaning of the fractions. Helena, for example, draws representations that show 24 objects, but the pictures do not show fourths or twelfths.

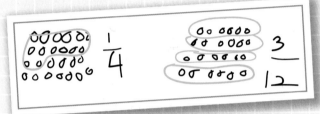

Helena's Work

Helena should be asked to explain her drawing. If necessary, use a context that is more familiar to her. For example:

You have 24 apples to share. If you give me $\frac{1}{4}$ of them, how many will I get? Show me with cubes (or a picture). Show me four equal groups of apples. What if 12 people shared the apples? How many apples would one person get? Let's look at the cubes again.

Richard seems to know that fractions have something to do with equal groups and that multiplying or dividing are operations about equal groups. He does successfully find $\frac{1}{4}$ of 24, but he seems confused as he tries to manipulate the numbers 3, 12, and 24 to find $\frac{3}{12}$ of 24. He seems to treat the numbers 3 and 12 as if they represent separate whole numbers.

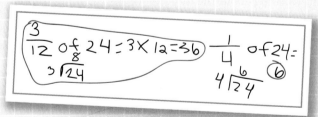

Richard's Work

Richard and Helena can both benefit from continuing work on identifying fractions of both rectangles and groups.

Problem 2

Benchmark addressed:

Benchmark 4: Order fractions with like and unlike denominators.

In order to meet the benchmark, students' work should show that they can:

- Place the fractions in the order $\frac{3}{6}, \frac{2}{3}, \frac{3}{4}, \frac{9}{8}, \frac{3}{2}$ on the number line. The numbers should be placed in order on the line relative to other numbers and relative to the landmarks; that is, the placement of $\frac{9}{8}$ should show that it is a little more than 1 and less than $\frac{3}{2}$;

- Understand the meaning of the numerator and the denominator in a fraction; in particular, recognize which fractions are more than 1.

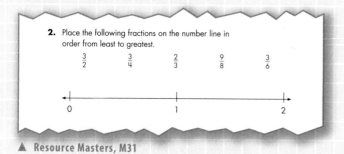

2. Place the following fractions on the number line in order from least to greatest.

$$\frac{3}{2} \qquad \frac{3}{4} \qquad \frac{2}{3} \qquad \frac{9}{8} \qquad \frac{3}{6}$$

▲ Resource Masters, M31

Meeting the Benchmark

Students who meet the benchmark have a solid understanding of the value of fractions. They recognize that $\frac{3}{6} = \frac{1}{2}$. They know that $\frac{3}{4}$ is midway between $\frac{1}{2}$ and one. They recognize which fractions are less than or more than 1. They are able to correctly order $\frac{2}{3}$ and $\frac{3}{4}$, usually by reasoning about the difference of each fraction from 1. Although students are not asked to provide an explanation of their work, some students might draw pictures as they work to compare some of the fractions.

Jill has placed the fractions in correct order, in the correct sections of the number line (either between 0 and 1 or between 1 and 2), and in reasonable places relative to each other and to the landmarks on the number line.

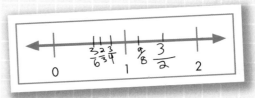

Jill's Work

Partially Meeting the Benchmark

Some students place many of the fractions accurately but have difficulties with particular fractions. For example, Derek places all the fractions correctly except for $\frac{2}{3}$ and $\frac{3}{4}$. He can distinguish between fractions that are less than and more than 1, and he places the fractions in reasonable places with respect to the landmarks 0, 1, and 2.

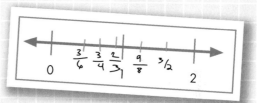

Derek's Work

Can Derek represent $\frac{2}{3}$ and $\frac{3}{4}$ as parts of a rectangle or as parts of a group of things? Does he know which is larger, $\frac{1}{3}$ or $\frac{1}{4}$? Can he use that knowledge to reason about $\frac{2}{3}$ and $\frac{3}{4}$?

Benson can also distinguish between fractions less than and greater than 1. He appears to know that $\frac{3}{6}$ is equivalent to $\frac{1}{2}$, and he places the rest of the fractions between the correct landmarks. However, he is not able to determine whether $\frac{2}{3}$ or $\frac{3}{4}$ is larger or whether $\frac{3}{2}$ or $\frac{9}{8}$ is larger.

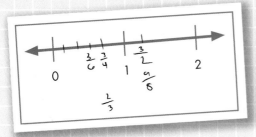

Benson's Work

Some students may still be having difficulty identifying fractions that are greater than 1, which is an indication that they do not yet have a complete understanding of the meaning of the numerator and denominator. Ursula places all the fractions under 1 in the correct order but $\frac{9}{8}$ and $\frac{3}{2}$ are included between 0 and 1.

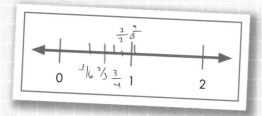

Ursula's Work

These students can all benefit from continuing to play *Capture Fractions* and can continue using their Fraction Cards to order subsets of the cards on the number line. You can choose a subset of the cards that contains many fractions with which they are familiar and a few of the fractions that are difficult for them. See further suggestions about fractions that are greater than 1 in the **Teacher Note:** Keeping Track of the Whole, page 149.

Not Meeting the Benchmark

Some students may still be struggling with the meaning and value of fractions. They may be able to identify and compare unit fractions (fractions that have a numerator of 1, such as $\frac{1}{3}$ and $\frac{1}{5}$) but they may not be able to interpret fractions with numerators greater than 1.

In the following example, Richard places the fractions almost randomly. Although $\frac{3}{4}$ and $\frac{2}{3}$ are correctly placed between 0 and 1, $\frac{3}{6}$ is placed at 2. It may be that Richard knows something about how a fraction can indicate division and divides 6 by 3 to get 2. However, his placement of $\frac{3}{2}$, $\frac{3}{6}$, and $\frac{9}{8}$ indicates that he does not have a grasp of the meaning of the numerator and denominator.

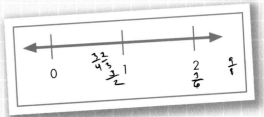

Richard's Work

Richard should use a context or representation to help him think through the value of each fraction. Choose a context that will be familiar to him.

We have 24 apples. I want to share them among 6 people. How many would each person get? What fraction of all the apples would that be? How many apples would $\frac{3}{6}$ be?

You may also ask him to shade in $\frac{1}{6}$ on a 4 × 6 rectangle. Then ask him to shade in $\frac{3}{6}$. Remind him that he is finding 3 of 6 equal parts. Students like Richard can benefit from continuing to represent fractional parts in this way and to solve story problems such as those on *Student Activity Book* page 6.

Problem 3

Benchmark addressed:

Benchmark 5: Read, write, and interpret decimal fractions in tenths and hundredths.

In order to meet the benchmark, students' work should show that they can:

- Compare these quantities using representations or by reasoning about the meaning of the numbers.

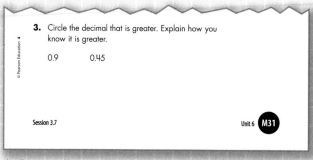

3. Circle the decimal that is greater. Explain how you know it is greater.

0.9   0.45

© Pearson Education 4

Session 3.7   Unit 6 **M31**

▲ **Resource Masters, M31**

Meeting the Benchmark

Students who meet the benchmark know that 0.9 is greater than 0.45. They are able to explain how they know by using representations of the two numbers, by reasoning about the place value of the digits in the two numbers, or by relating each decimal to a landmark.

Luke correctly identifies 0.9 as greater than 0.45 by relating each to landmarks he knows.

> .9 is 1 tenth away from one whole And
> I know that .45 is close to .5 which
> is less than 1. So .9 is more.

Luke's Work

Helena also knows that 0.9 is greater than 0.45. She uses knowledge of place value.

> I know that .9 is more because .9
> has 9 in the tenths place and .45 has
> a 4 in the tenths place.

Helena's Work

Partially Meeting the Benchmark

Students who partially meet the benchmark may know which decimal is greater, but their explanations do not show full understanding. For example, Ursula is correct in determining that 0.9 is greater than 0.45, but it is unclear from her explanation whether she knows why.

> .9 is more because it is a much
> bigger number than .45

Ursula's Work

Ask students like Ursula to expand their explanation, either by using a representation or by reference to the place value of the digits in these numbers.

Not Meeting the Benchmark

Students who do not meet the benchmark are not able to interpret numbers with decimal portions in the tenths and hundredths. They either do not solve the problem, solve it incorrectly, or are not able to provide any reasoning to justify their answer. Some of these students may be able to compare decimals that are both tenths but cannot compare tenths to hundredths, as in this problem. For example, Yuki incorrectly determines that 0.45 is greater than 0.9 because he is reading these decimals as if they were whole numbers.

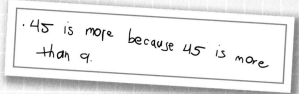

> .45 is more because 45 is more
> than 9.

Yuki's Work

Can Yuki draw either of these fractions as part of a rectangle? Can he interpret 0.9 as $\frac{9}{10}$? Does he know that 0.9 is close to 1? Students who do not meet the benchmark can benefit from continuing to represent decimals as parts of a square and to play *Decimal Compare*.

Finding Combinations That Equal 1

In the Math Workshop in Session 1.6, some students are working on the activity Combinations That Equal 1. A pair of students is looking at the following divisions they have made of the 4 × 6 rectangle:

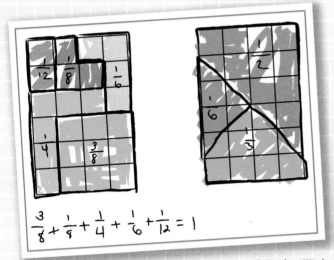

$$\frac{3}{8} + \frac{1}{9} + \frac{1}{4} + \frac{1}{6} + \frac{1}{12} = 1$$

Sample Student Work

They are discussing whether the fractions are labeled accurately in their second example and whether they add up to 1. The teacher listens and decides that these students are ready to move their reasoning from counting squares to using reasoning about relationships among the fractions.

Nadeem: I don't know if the $\frac{1}{2}$ section is really $\frac{1}{2}$.

Tonya: I know that there are 24 squares in the whole rectangle, so there have to be 12 to make it $\frac{1}{2}$. Let's count.

Both students count up the squares. They can easily count the whole units (10) and agree that the four halves add up to two.

Tonya: So that is $\frac{1}{2}$. How many squares are $\frac{1}{3}$?

Nadeem: Well, three goes into 24 eight times. So $\frac{1}{3}$ is eight squares. Are there eight squares in the $\frac{1}{3}$ space?

Again, they both count and agree that there are eight squares.

Teacher: Before you work on the $\frac{1}{6}$ piece of the rectangle, besides counting, is there a way you could figure out whether that piece is exactly $\frac{1}{6}$ of the whole?

Nadeem: $\frac{1}{6}$ is half of $\frac{1}{3}$ so it has to have 4 squares. [Nadeem counts.] And it does—so it is $\frac{1}{6}$.

Teacher: Is there any other way you could make sure that it is $\frac{1}{6}$? [The teacher pauses, but there is no answer from either student.] You seem sure that you have $\frac{1}{3}$ and $\frac{1}{2}$. And I know you know that $\frac{1}{2} + \frac{1}{2} = 1$ whole.

Tonya: Oh! $\frac{1}{3} + \frac{1}{6} = \frac{1}{2}$. So that little piece has to be $\frac{1}{6}$ to make it all 1 whole. Do you see, Nadeem?

Nadeem: I think so.

Teacher: Go ahead and record your addition equation under your rectangle: $\frac{1}{2} + \frac{1}{3} + \frac{1}{6} = 1$.

The teacher asks both students to think about the relationships among the fractional parts and their relationship to 1. Because they can see that the three parts together make up the whole rectangle, they need to complete the equation $\frac{1}{2} + \frac{1}{3} + \underline{\quad} = 1$. The teacher wants them to consider how they can be sure what the third fractional part is without counting squares. It is unclear whether Nadeem is convinced that $\frac{1}{3} + \frac{1}{6} = \frac{1}{2}$ and it would be useful to ask him to model that equation on a rectangle. Many students learned this combination from their work with pattern blocks in Grade 3, and some students may find the pattern blocks helpful in reviewing some of these relationships.

Dialogue Box

Comparing Fractions to Landmarks

This Grade 4 class is working on the activity Comparing Fractions to Landmarks in Session 2.4. They are sorting their Fraction Cards and placing them on a number line in relationship to the landmark numbers 0, $\frac{1}{2}$, 1, and 2. The teacher listens and questions a group about how they are making their decisions as they work.

Ramona: I'm going to put $\frac{1}{3}$ between 0 and $\frac{1}{2}$. Does everyone agree?

Jill: I do. It's definitely not more than $\frac{1}{2}$.

Teacher: Why do you say that, Jill?

Jill: I know that $\frac{1}{3}$ of a rectangle is less than one half of the rectangle because when you break a rectangle into three pieces instead of two, the pieces of three are smaller than the pieces of two.

Teacher: What if the fraction was $\frac{2}{3}$? Where would that go?

Bill: That would go after the $\frac{1}{2}$ because $\frac{1}{3}$ is less than $\frac{1}{2}$ but $\frac{2}{3}$ is more than $\frac{1}{2}$.

Teacher: But how do you know that? I know that you can see it on your cards, but can anyone explain it—as if you were explaining it to a third grader?

Yuki: It is bigger than $\frac{1}{2}$ but smaller than 1. It is definitely smaller than 1 because $\frac{3}{3}$ would be 1 whole and $\frac{2}{3}$ is less.

Bill: And you know it has to be more than $\frac{1}{2}$ because look, there are three pieces if it's thirds, and so it takes one and a half pieces to make one half, but $\frac{2}{3}$ is two of the pieces, so it's more.

Ramona: Uh oh, look at this one. $\frac{5}{3}$. Where does this one go?

Yuki: It goes between 1 and 2. I think it's larger than 1 because 1 is $\frac{3}{3}$ and $\frac{5}{3}$ is $\frac{2}{3}$ more than $\frac{3}{3}$, so $\frac{5}{3}$ is bigger than 1.

Jill: I agree. If the top number is bigger than the bottom number it is bigger than 1 whole. It's one of the conjectures on our list.

Bill: But how do you know that it is?

Teacher: This is what you were saying you didn't get the other day. Can you say again what you were saying about a fraction like $\frac{5}{3}$?

Bill: I get it a little better now, but I was saying how can you have five thirds when you can only have three thirds?

Teacher: So what do you mean, "you get it a little better now"?

Bill: When Tonya was saying yesterday that $\frac{5}{3}$ is just the same as 1 and $\frac{2}{3}$. That makes more sense to me. If it's a sandwich, it's one whole sandwich and $\frac{2}{3}$ of another one.

Ramona: It's just another way to say it. Three thirds and two thirds is five thirds, or it's one and two thirds.

Bill: I still think that five thirds sounds weird, though.

Teacher: Yuki used what he knew about 1 to help him decide where $\frac{5}{3}$ goes. If we added $1\frac{1}{2}$ to our landmark fractions, where would you put $\frac{5}{3}$? Is it bigger or smaller than $1\frac{1}{2}$?

Yuki: Like Bill and I said, $\frac{2}{3}$ is bigger than $\frac{1}{2}$, so $1\frac{2}{3}$ is also bigger than $1\frac{1}{2}$.

Bill: The next card is $\frac{2}{6}$. Where would $\frac{2}{6}$ go?

Ramona: On top of $\frac{1}{3}$ because $\frac{2}{6}$ is equal to $\frac{1}{3}$.

Teacher: How do you know that they're equal?

Jill: When I look at the part that's colored in my Fraction Card, they're the same.

Teacher: Again, could you explain it more? If you weren't looking right at the cards, how could you convince me?

Jill: When you cut thirds in half, you get sixths. First you have three pieces, and then you have six pieces. Each of the thirds makes two sixths when you cut it in half.

In this discussion, the teacher encourages students to explain their reasoning to one another and to extend their thinking (is $\frac{5}{3}$ more or less than $1\frac{1}{2}$?). The teacher wants her students to use the pictures on their Fraction Cards to help them visualize relationships between fractions and landmarks such as $\frac{1}{2}$ and 1, but she also wants them to use what they know about fractions to reason about the relative size of the fractions they are placing on their number line. When Jill says, "I look at the part that's colored in my Fraction Card," the teacher asks for further explanation.

Similarly, when students simply assert that one fraction is smaller than another, as when Bill compares $\frac{1}{2}$ and $\frac{2}{3}$, the teacher asks further questions. The teacher also pursues Bill's comment about $\frac{5}{3}$ because a number of students are not clear about the meaning of fractions greater than 1. Although the teacher is fairly confident that Jill can articulate good reasoning to back up her assertion that "If the top number is bigger than the bottom number, it is bigger than one whole," rules like this are sometimes readily adopted by other students without the understanding that Jill has, so the teacher wants to get a sense of how others in the group are interpreting the meaning of $\frac{5}{3}$.

Dialogue Box

Conjectures About Fractions

As students work on their Fraction Number Lines, the class has been listing conjectures about comparing fractions. In the discussion at the end of Session 2.6, the teacher focuses on two of the ideas many of the students have been using.

Teacher: You've come up with quite a few conjectures about rules for comparing fractions. One that I notice many of you have been using is this one [points to the chart]: *If the denominators of two fractions are the same, the one with the larger numerator is larger.* Benson, weren't you using this idea when you were trying to decide where to put $\frac{6}{8}$ on the number line?

Benson: $\frac{6}{8}$ would go in here [points to a spot midway between $\frac{1}{2}$ and 1 on the class fraction number line] because $\frac{4}{8}$ would be equivalent to $\frac{1}{2}$. So because 6 is greater than 4, then it would be more pieces of 8, so $\frac{6}{8}$ would be bigger than $\frac{1}{2}$. It wouldn't be $\frac{8}{8}$ so it would be between $\frac{1}{2}$ and 1.

Teacher: Does this idea work with any pair of fractions? If the denominators are the same, but the numerators are different, the one with the larger numerator is a larger fraction? What is another pair of fractions like this?

Sabrina: $\frac{2}{4}$ and $\frac{3}{4}$. That's an easy one. $\frac{3}{4}$ is larger.

Andrew: $\frac{5}{12}$ and $\frac{11}{12}$. $\frac{11}{12}$ has to be bigger because it's 11 of the twelfths.

Teacher: Benson said that it would be "more pieces of eight" and Andrew said that "it's 11 of the twelfths." Do you think this idea works with any pair of fractions with the same denominators? Do you think it's always true?

Marisol: It has to be because you're breaking something into the same number of pieces but you're taking more of them.

Anna: It's like if you had pizza. You cut it into 8 slices. One slice is $\frac{1}{8}$. If I eat $\frac{3}{8}$ and you eat $\frac{5}{8}$, you ate 5 slices. You ate more.

Teacher: Here's what I think Marisol and Anna are saying (quickly sketches a circle divided into eight equal pieces). They're saying that $\frac{3}{8}$ is three of the 8 slices, and $\frac{5}{8}$ is five of the 8 slices, so it's more slices. Can anyone use this pizza story and picture to talk about why this would be true for any pair of fractions with the same denominators? Would it work for $\frac{5}{19}$ and $\frac{8}{19}$ or $\frac{7}{10}$ and $\frac{9}{10}$?

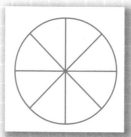

Jake: It has to work. It doesn't matter how many pieces you make. Whatever the number of pieces, that's the denominator. So if you take more of the pieces, you are taking more of the whole pizza.

Lucy: You could have 100 pieces, and still if one person has $\frac{3}{100}$ and one person has $\frac{19}{100}$, the person with the higher numerator has more. The higher number is more of the same thing.

Teacher: You have some good arguments for comparing fractions with the same denominator. Let's look at one of your other conjectures, which is about fractions that have the same numerators. The conjecture we wrote down is this: *If two fractions have the same numerator, the one with the larger denominator is a smaller fraction.* First of all, what are some examples of fractions that have the same numerator but different denominators?

After listing some examples, the discussion continues.

Ursula: Ummm . . . it's like when I was putting $\frac{2}{6}$ on the number line, and I didn't know whether it went before $\frac{1}{4}$ or after it. So I knew $\frac{2}{6}$ is equal to $\frac{1}{3}$ and they both have 1 at the top. 4 is smaller than 6, so it's bigger. $\frac{1}{4}$ comes after $\frac{1}{6}$.

Teacher: You're saying that $\frac{1}{4}$ and $\frac{1}{6}$ have the same numerator, but 4 is smaller than 6, so $\frac{1}{4}$ is larger. But how do you know that works for these two fractions or for other pairs of fractions like this?

Venetta: You can do it the same way, with pizzas. I could eat $\frac{1}{4}$ of a pizza and you could eat $\frac{1}{6}$ of a pizza. I'd eat more.

Teacher: Is there a way I could draw that on the board?

Venetta: Draw one with four slices and one with six slices. The one with four slices has bigger slices, so one of the four slices is more than one of the six slices.

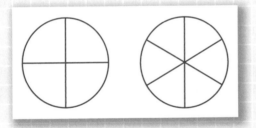

Teacher: Who can say anything else about this?

Enrique It's like when I was doing $\frac{5}{3}$ and $\frac{5}{4}$. I didn't know which one came first. But then I thought about thirds and fourths. Thirds are bigger parts, so each of the thirds is bigger than each of the fourths, so the whole thing is bigger.

The teacher helps students start with particular examples and then use those examples to state more general ideas about the fraction relationships. Lucy says, "The higher number is more of the same thing." Jake says, "Whatever the number of pieces, that's the denominator. So if you take more of the pieces, you are taking more of the whole pizza." In these statements, Lucy and Jake are making general claims about all pairs of fractions with the same denominator. As students talk, the teacher uses familiar fraction representations so that all students can visualize the relationships to which students refer in their arguments and have the chance to build on those ideas themselves.

Are These Equal?

In Session 3.3, these three students are discussing the values of $\frac{3}{10}$, 0.3, and $\frac{30}{100}$ in order to answer the question "Are these three numbers equal?" The teacher listens to them for a few minutes and encourages them to model their thinking on a 10×10 square to make sure that they all agree.

Amelia: They all look different to me. But I don't know how to figure out which is bigger and which is smaller.

Nadeem: We have two fractions and one decimal. Fractions and decimals can be written either way. I think we should change 0.3 into a fraction. What would it be?

Luke: It would be $\frac{3}{10}$. Oh, so $\frac{3}{10}$ and $\frac{30}{100}$ are the same, right? So we know two of them are the same.

Amelia: I guess so.

Teacher: How do you know that 0.3 and $\frac{30}{100}$ are the same? What would each look like on a square?

Amelia draws on two squares as Luke and Nadeem watch.

Amelia: 0 point 3 is three columns of squares. That's 30 squares of the 100 squares. [She starts coloring 30 squares in and then stops.] Oh, yeah, they are the same. They are both 30 out of 100.

Luke: And $\frac{3}{10}$ is the same, too. Because it is three rows [he points to the three columns Amelia has almost drawn in] out of ten rows. So all three are the same.

Teacher: Are there other fractions and decimal numbers that are equal to these as well?

The class ends before they can answer the question, but the teacher decides to pose it to the whole class at the start of the next session.

Student Math Handbook

The *Student Math Handbook* pages related to this unit are pictured on the following pages. This book is designed to be used flexibly: as a resource for students doing classwork, as a book students can take home for reference while doing homework and playing math games with their families, and as a reference for families to better understand the work their children are doing in class.

When students take the *Student Math Handbook* home, they and their families can discuss these pages together to reinforce or enhance students' understanding of the mathematical concepts and games in this unit.

Addition Strategies
(page 1 of 2)

In Grade 4, you are using different strategies to solve addition problems efficiently. Here is an example:

$$1,852 + 688$$

Breaking the Numbers Apart

Cheyenne solved this problem by adding one number in parts.

Cheyenne's solution

$1,852 + 688 =$

$1,852 + 600 = 2,452$
$2,452 + 80 = 2,532$
$2,532 + 8 = \mathbf{2,540}$

Richard and Jill solved the problem by adding by place. Their solutions are similar, but they recorded their work differently.

Richard's solution

$1,800 + 600 =$ $2,400$
$50 + 80 =$ 130
$2 + 8 =$ $\underline{10}$
     $\mathbf{2,540}$

Jill's solution

$$\begin{array}{r} 1,852 \\ + \ 688 \\ \hline 1,000 \\ 1,400 \\ 130 \\ + \ \ 10 \\ \hline \mathbf{2,540} \end{array}$$

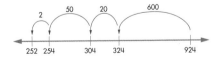

SMH
8   eight

Addition Strategies
(page 2 of 2)

$$1,852 + 688$$

Changing the Numbers

Emaan solved the problem by changing one number and adjusting the sum. He changed 688 to 700 to make an easier problem to solve.

Emaan's solution

$$\begin{array}{r} 1,852 \\ + \ 700 \\ \hline 2,552 \\ - \ \ 12 \\ \hline \mathbf{2,540} \end{array}$$ *I added 700 instead of 688.*

         Then I subtracted the extra 12.

Venetta solved this problem by creating an equivalent problem.

Venetta's solution

$1,852 + 688 =$
$(-12) \ \ \ (+12)$ *I added 12 to 688 and subtracted 12 from 1,852.*
$1,840 + 700 = \mathbf{2,540}$

?   Show how you would solve the problem 1,852 + 688.

nine   SMH **9**

Subtraction Strategies
(page 1 of 3)

In Grade 4, you are using different strategies to solve subtraction problems efficiently. Here is an example:

$$924 - 672$$

Subtracting in Parts

Amelia solved this problem by subtracting in parts.

Amelia's solution

$924 - 672 =$

$924 - 600 = 324$
$324 - 20 = 304$
$304 - 50 = 254$
$254 - 2 = \mathbf{252}$

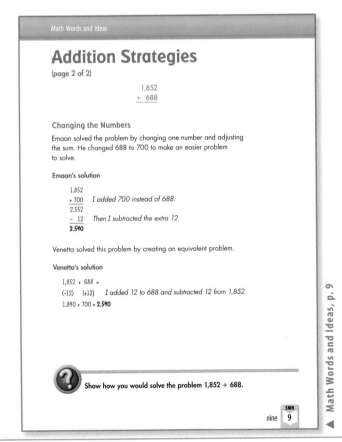

I started at 924, and jumped back 672 in four parts (−600, −20, −50, −2).
I landed on 252.
The answer is the place where I landed.

$924 - 672 = \mathbf{252}$

thirteen   SMH **13**

Subtraction Strategies

(page 2 of 3)

$$924$$
$$- 672$$

Adding Up

200   28 24

672   872 900 924

Jake used an adding-up strategy to solve 924 − 672.

Jake's solution

672 + ___?___ = 924

672 + __200__ = 872

872 + __28__ = 900

900 + __24__ = 924

200 + 28 + 24 = **252**   *The answer is the total of all of the jumps from 672 up to 924.*

Subtracting Back

28   200   24

672 700   900 924

Luke used a subtracting-back strategy.

Luke's solution

924 − __24__ = 900

900 − __200__ = 700

700 − __28__ = 672

24 + 200 + 28 = **252**   *The answer is the total of all the jumps from 924 back to 672.*

SMH
14 fourteen

▲ Math Words and Ideas, p. 14

Subtraction Strategies

(page 3 of 3)

$$924$$
$$- 672$$

Changing the Numbers

Sabrina and Ursula solved 924 − 672 by changing the numbers to make an easier problem to solve.

Sabrina's solution

Sabrina changed one number and then adjusted to find her answer.

680

8

244 252   924

924 − 672 =

924 − 680 = 244   *I subtracted 680 instead of 672.*

244 + 8 = **252**   *I subtracted too much, so I have to add 8 back on.*

Ursula's solution

Ursula solved this problem by creating an equivalent problem.

672 700   924 952

924 − 672 =

(+28) (+28)

952 − 700 = **252**

? Show how you would solve the problem 924 − 672.

fifteen SMH **15**

▲ Math Words and Ideas, p. 15

Fractions

Math Words
• fraction
• numerator
• denominator

Fractions are numbers.

Some fractions, like $\frac{1}{2}$ and $\frac{3}{4}$, are less than 1.

Some fractions, like $\frac{2}{2}$ and $\frac{4}{4}$, are equal to 1.

Some fractions, like $\frac{6}{4}$ and $\frac{3}{2}$, are greater than 1.

Fraction Notation

The denominator is the total number of equal shares. → $\frac{3}{4}$ ← The numerator is the number of equal shares out of the total.

three fourths

One third of Austria's flag is white.

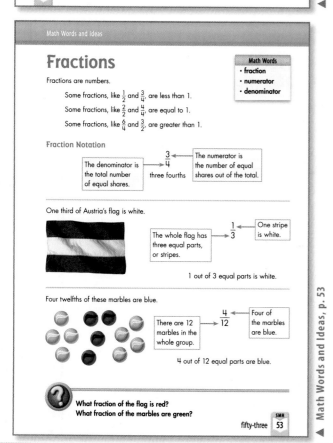

The whole flag has three equal parts, or stripes. → $\frac{1}{3}$ ← One stripe is white.

1 out of 3 equal parts is white.

Four twelfths of these marbles are blue.

There are 12 marbles in the whole group. → $\frac{4}{12}$ ← Four of the marbles are blue.

4 out of 12 equal parts are blue.

? What fraction of the flag is red?
What fraction of the marbles are green?

fifty-three SMH **53**

▲ Math Words and Ideas, p. 53

Fractions of an Area

Enrique, Helena, Amelia, and Luke have one sandwich to share equally. How much of the sandwich will each of them get?

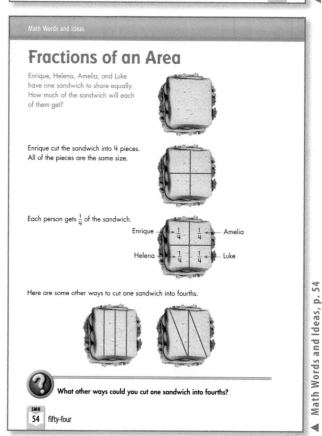

Enrique cut the sandwich into 4 pieces. All of the pieces are the same size.

Each person gets $\frac{1}{4}$ of the sandwich.

Enrique → $\frac{1}{4}$ $\frac{1}{4}$ ← Amelia

Helena → $\frac{1}{4}$ $\frac{1}{4}$ ← Luke

Here are some other ways to cut one sandwich into fourths.

? What other ways could you cut one sandwich into fourths?

SMH **54** fifty-four

▲ Math Words and Ideas, p. 54

Fractions of a Group of Objects

Three people shared 18 apples equally. Each person gets $\frac{1}{3}$ of the apples.

$\frac{1}{3}$ ⟶ 1 group for each person
⟶ 3 equal groups

$\frac{1}{3}$ of 18 is **6**.

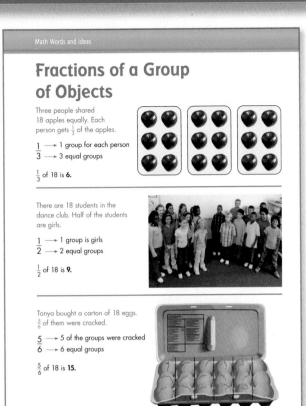

There are 18 students in the dance club. Half of the students are girls.

$\frac{1}{2}$ ⟶ 1 group is girls
⟶ 2 equal groups

$\frac{1}{2}$ of 18 is **9**.

Tonya bought a carton of 18 eggs. $\frac{5}{6}$ of them were cracked.

$\frac{5}{6}$ ⟶ 5 of the groups were cracked
⟶ 6 equal groups

$\frac{5}{6}$ of 18 is **15**.

fifty-five **55**

◀ Math Words and Ideas, p. 55

Naming Fractional Parts

(page 1 of 2)

In each of these examples, one whole square has been divided into equal parts.

How much is blue?
1 out of 2 equal parts

How much is white?
1 out of 2 equal parts

$\frac{1}{2}$
one half

$\frac{1}{2}$
one half

How much is blue?
1 out of 4 equal parts

How much is white?
3 out of 4 equal parts

$\frac{1}{4}$
one fourth
one quarter

$\frac{3}{4}$
three fourths
three quarters

How much is blue?
1 out of 8 equal parts

How much is white?
7 out of 8 equal parts

$\frac{1}{8}$
one eighth

$\frac{7}{8}$
seven eighths

56 fifty-six

◀ Math Words and Ideas, p. 56

Naming Fractional Parts

(page 2 of 2)

How much is blue?
1 out of 3 equal parts

How much is white?
2 out of 3 equal parts

$\frac{1}{3}$
one third

$\frac{2}{3}$
two thirds

How much is blue?
1 out of 6 equal parts

How much is white?
5 out of 6 equal parts

$\frac{1}{6}$
one sixth

$\frac{5}{6}$
five sixths

Sabrina looked at all of these diagrams.

"It's interesting that 8 is the biggest number of parts, but that square has the smallest parts."

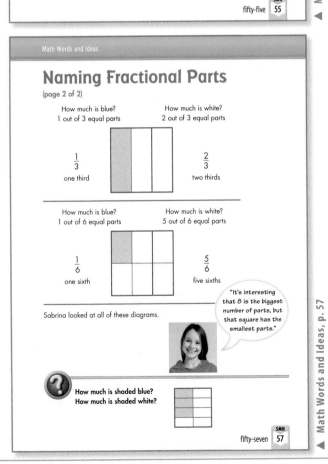

? How much is shaded blue?
How much is shaded white?

fifty-seven **57**

◀ Math Words and Ideas, p. 57

Using Fractions for Quantities Greater Than One

Math Words
· mixed number

To represent fractions greater than one, you need more than one whole.

In this diagram, each whole is divided into 6 equal parts. Six parts ($\frac{6}{6}$) are shaded on the first whole and one part ($\frac{1}{6}$) is shaded on the second whole.

$\frac{7}{6}$ or $1\frac{1}{6}$

The total amount shaded is $\frac{7}{6}$, or $1\frac{1}{6}$.

In this diagram, two whole squares are shaded. That equals 2. It also equals $\frac{8}{4}$. (Imagine each of the two shaded wholes divided into fourths.)

The last square is divided into four equal parts, and three parts are shaded. That equals $\frac{3}{4}$.

$2\frac{3}{4}$ or $\frac{11}{4}$

The total amount shaded is $\frac{11}{4}$ or $2\frac{3}{4}$.

A mixed number has a whole number part and a fractional part.

$2\frac{3}{4}$ — two and three fourths
two and three quarters

whole number | fraction

? Show how you can represent these fractional parts using squares. $\frac{4}{3}$ $1\frac{3}{8}$

58 fifty-eight

◀ Math Words and Ideas, p. 58

Equivalent Fractions

Math Words
· equivalent fractions

Different fractions that name the same amount are called equivalent fractions.

Benson used 4 × 6 rectangles to show some equivalent fractions.

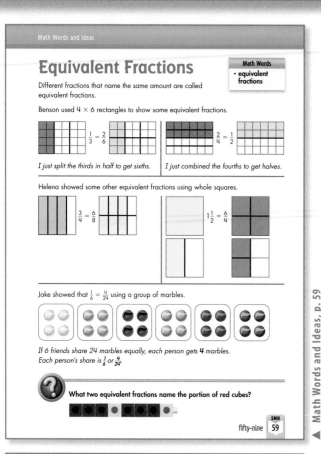

$\frac{1}{3} = \frac{2}{6}$

$\frac{2}{4} = \frac{1}{2}$

I just split the thirds in half to get sixths.   *I just combined the fourths to get halves.*

Helena showed some other equivalent fractions using whole squares.

$\frac{3}{4} = \frac{6}{8}$

$1\frac{1}{2} = \frac{6}{4}$

Jake showed that $\frac{1}{6} = \frac{4}{24}$ using a group of marbles.

If 6 friends share 24 marbles equally, each person gets 4 marbles.
Each person's share is $\frac{1}{6}$ or $\frac{4}{24}$.

? What two equivalent fractions name the portion of red cubes?

fifty-nine **SMH 59**

◄ Math Words and Ideas, p. 59

Comparing Fractions

(page 1 of 2)

Which is larger, $\frac{2}{5}$ or $\frac{5}{2}$?

Cheyenne drew pictures to solve the problem.

Cheyenne's solution

$\frac{2}{5}$ is less than 1 whole.

I drew $\frac{2}{5}$ by dividing the whole into 5 equal parts and then I shaded 2 parts.

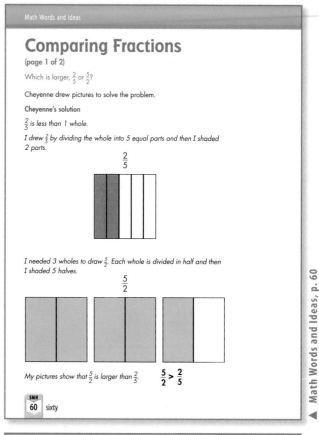

$\frac{2}{5}$

I needed 3 wholes to draw $\frac{5}{2}$. Each whole is divided in half and then I shaded 5 halves.

$\frac{5}{2}$

My pictures show that $\frac{5}{2}$ is larger than $\frac{2}{5}$. $\frac{5}{2} > \frac{2}{5}$

SMH 60 sixty

◄ Math Words and Ideas, p. 60

Comparing Fractions

(page 2 of 2)

Which is larger, $\frac{7}{8}$ or $\frac{5}{6}$?

Alejandro drew pictures to solve the problem.

Alejandro's solution

I shaded $\frac{7}{8}$ and $\frac{5}{6}$ on 4 × 6 grids.

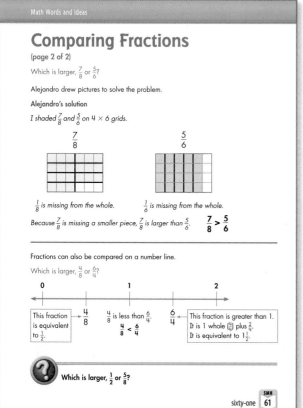

$\frac{7}{8}$

$\frac{5}{6}$

$\frac{1}{8}$ is missing from the whole. $\frac{1}{6}$ is missing from the whole.

Because $\frac{7}{8}$ is missing a smaller piece, $\frac{7}{8}$ is larger than $\frac{5}{6}$. $\frac{7}{8} > \frac{5}{6}$

Fractions can also be compared on a number line.

Which is larger, $\frac{4}{8}$ or $\frac{6}{4}$?

0   1   2

$\frac{4}{8}$ $\frac{6}{4}$

This fraction is equivalent to $\frac{1}{2}$.

$\frac{4}{8}$ is less than $\frac{6}{4}$. $\frac{4}{8} < \frac{6}{4}$

This fraction is greater than 1. It is 1 whole ($\frac{4}{4}$) plus $\frac{2}{4}$. It is equivalent to $1\frac{1}{2}$.

? Which is larger, $\frac{1}{2}$ or $\frac{5}{8}$?

sixty-one **SMH 61**

◄ Math Words and Ideas, p. 61

Adding Fractions

These students used representations to solve problems about adding fractions.

Kimberly had 24 baseball cards. She gave $\frac{1}{8}$ of the cards to her sister and $\frac{3}{8}$ of the cards to a friend. What fraction of her cards did Kimberly give away?

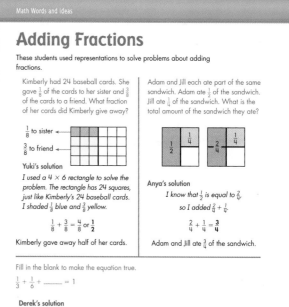

$\frac{1}{8}$ to sister

$\frac{3}{8}$ to friend

Yuki's solution

I used a 4 × 6 rectangle to solve the problem. The rectangle has 24 squares, just like Kimberly's 24 baseball cards. I shaded $\frac{1}{8}$ blue and $\frac{3}{8}$ yellow.

$\frac{1}{8} + \frac{3}{8} = \frac{4}{8}$ or $\frac{1}{2}$

Kimberly gave away half of her cards.

Adam and Jill each ate part of the same sandwich. Adam ate $\frac{1}{2}$ of the sandwich. Jill ate $\frac{1}{4}$ of the sandwich. What is the total amount of the sandwich they ate?

$\frac{1}{2}$ $\frac{1}{4}$ $\frac{2}{4}$ $\frac{1}{4}$

Anya's solution

I know that $\frac{1}{2}$ is equal to $\frac{2}{4}$, so I added $\frac{2}{4} + \frac{1}{4}$.

$\frac{2}{4} + \frac{1}{4} = \frac{3}{4}$

Adam and Jill ate $\frac{3}{4}$ of the sandwich.

Fill in the blank to make the equation true.

$\frac{1}{3} + \frac{1}{6} +$ _____ $= 1$

Derek's solution

$\frac{1}{3}$ $\frac{1}{6}$?

I used a 5 × 12 rectangle to solve the problem.

$\frac{1}{3}$ covers 20 out of 60 square units and $\frac{1}{6}$ covers 10 square units. That leaves 30 square units, which is $\frac{1}{2}$ of the rectangle. The missing fraction is $\frac{1}{2}$.

$\frac{1}{3} + \frac{1}{6} + \frac{1}{2} = 1$

SMH 62 sixty-two

◄ Math Words and Ideas, p. 62

Math Words and Ideas

Halves of Different Wholes

Steve shaded $\frac{1}{2}$ of this 4 × 6 rectangle.

Steve's solution

I know that the shaded part is $\frac{1}{2}$ because the whole rectangle has 24 square units and the shaded part has 12 square units, and 2 × 12 = 24.

Ramona shaded $\frac{1}{2}$ of this 5 × 12 rectangle.

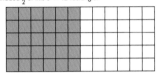

Ramona's solution

I know that the shaded part is $\frac{1}{2}$ because I drew a line in the middle of the rectangle. There are 30 shaded squares and 30 unshaded squares.

Half of the 4 × 6 rectangle is smaller than half of the 5 × 12 rectangle because the whole 4 × 6 rectangle is smaller than the whole 5 × 12 rectangle.

 How many square units are in $\frac{1}{2}$ of this 10 × 10 square?

sixty-three **SMH 63**

▲ Math Words and Ideas, p. 63

Math Words and Ideas

Decimals

Math Words
• decimal
• decimal point

The system we use to write numbers is called the decimal number system. *Decimal* means that the number is based on tens.

Some numbers, like 2.5 and 0.3, include a decimal point. The digits to the right of the decimal point are the part of the number that is less than 1.

Here are some examples of decimal numbers you may know that are less than one.

$$0.5 = \frac{5}{10} = \frac{1}{2} \qquad 0.25 = \frac{25}{100} = \frac{1}{4}$$

Numbers such as 0.5 and 0.25 are sometimes called decimal fractions.

Some decimal numbers have a whole number part and a part that is less than 1, just as mixed numbers do.

$$1.5 = 1\frac{5}{10} = 1\frac{1}{2} \qquad 12.75 = 12\frac{75}{100} = 12\frac{3}{4}$$

Here are some examples of the ways we use decimals everyday:

Derek bought 0.5 pound of cheese.

The race is a little more than 26 miles.

The T-shirt costs a little less than $10.

 Write a decimal number that is. . . a little more than 5.
. . . almost 17.
. . . more than $\frac{1}{2}$ and less than 1.

SMH 64 sixty-four

▲ Math Words and Ideas, p. 64

Math Words and Ideas

Representing Decimals

Math Words
• one tenth
• one hundredth
• one thousandth

This square represents one whole.

In each of the following examples, the whole square has been divided into equal parts and the amount shaded is named.

This square is divided into 10 parts.

One out of the ten parts is shaded.

Amount shaded: one tenth

fraction: $\frac{1}{10}$

decimal: 0.1

This square is divided into 100 parts.

One out of the 100 parts is shaded.

Amount shaded: one hundredth

fraction: $\frac{1}{100}$

decimal: 0.01

This square is divided into 1,000 parts.

One out of the 1,000 parts is shaded.

Amount shaded: one thousandth

fraction: $\frac{1}{1000}$

decimal: 0.001

sixty-five **SMH 65**

▲ Math Words and Ideas, p. 65

Math Words and Ideas

Place Value of Decimals

(page 1 of 2)

Math Words
• place value
• decimal point

As with whole numbers, the value of a digit changes depending on its place in a decimal number.

thousands place	hundreds place	tens place	ones place	decimal point	tenths place	hundredths place	thousandths place

In these two examples, the digit 5 has different values.

0.5

The digit 5 in the tenths place represents $\frac{5}{10}$.

0.45

The digit 5 in the hundredths place represents $\frac{5}{100}$.

 What are the values of the digits in this number? 0.39

SMH 66 sixty-six

▲ Math Words and Ideas, p. 66

Place Value of Decimals

(page 2 of 2)

Look at the values of the digits in this number:

2.75

two and seventy-five hundredths

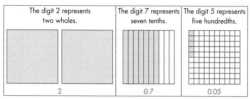

The digit 2 represents two wholes.	The digit 7 represents seven tenths.	The digit 5 represents five hundredths.
2	0.7	0.05

2.75 = 2 + 0.7 + 0.05

For decimals greater than one, read the whole number, say "and" for the decimal point, then read the decimal.

Here are some more examples:

10.5	200.05	17.45
ten and five tenths	two hundred and five hundredths	seventeen and forty-five hundredths

How would you say this number?
40.35
How would you write this number?
three hundred five and four tenths

Math Words and Ideas, p. 67

Tenths and Hundredths

How many tenths are shaded?

0.5 5 out of 10 columns are shaded.

How many hundredths are shaded?

0.50 50 out of 100 squares are shaded.

These decimals are equal: 0.5 = 0.50

There are many ways to represent the same part of a whole with decimals and fractions.

$$0.5 = 0.50 = \frac{1}{2} = \frac{5}{10} = \frac{50}{100}$$

How many tenths are shaded?

0.2 2 out of 10 columns are shaded.

How many hundredths are shaded?

0.20 20 out of 100 squares are shaded.

$$0.2 = 0.20 = \frac{2}{10} = \frac{1}{5} = \frac{20}{100}$$

How many tenths are shaded?
How many hundredths are shaded?
What fractional part is shaded?

Math Words and Ideas, p. 68

Comparing Decimals

Anna and Luke both walk to school from their homes.
Anna walks 0.35 miles.
Luke walks 0.6 miles.
Who walks farther?

LaTanya's solution

I used a number line from 0 to 1. First I marked $\frac{1}{2}$. Then I marked tenths. I know that $\frac{1}{2}$ mile is the same as 0.5. Luke walks 0.6 miles, which is a little more than $\frac{1}{2}$. Anna walks 0.35 miles, which is between 0.3 and 0.4 miles and is less than $\frac{1}{2}$. So, Luke walks farther than Anna.

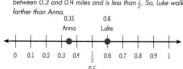

Kimberly's solution

0.35 is three and a half tenths.
0.6 is six tenths, so it is larger.

Damian's solution

I thought 0.35 was bigger because it has more numbers in it. But when I drew the picture I saw that 0.6 is the same as $\frac{60}{100}$, which is greater than $\frac{35}{100}$.

35 is greater than 6, but 0.35 is not greater than 0.6.

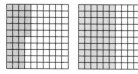

0.35 < 0.6

Math Words and Ideas, p. 69

Adding Decimals (page 1 of 2)

0.5 + 0.6 =

Helena's solution

I added 0.5 and 0.6.

0.5 is $\frac{1}{2}$.   0.6 is $\frac{1}{2}$ and one more tenth.

So 5 tenths plus 6 tenths equal one whole and one tenth.
0.5 + 0.6 = **1.1**

I checked my work by shading the decimals on these 10 × 10 squares.

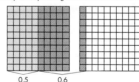

0.5   0.6

0.5 + 0.25 =

Bill's solution

I shaded both decimals on a 10 × 10 square, using different colors.

I shaded 0.5 in green. I shaded 0.25 in blue.

That is 2 more tenths and 5 hundredths.

The total is 7 tenths and 5 hundredths or **0.75**.

Marisol's solution

I know that $0.5 = \frac{1}{2}$ and $0.25 = \frac{1}{4}$, so I can add the fractions instead and get the same answer.

$\frac{1}{2} + \frac{1}{4} = \frac{3}{4}$. $\frac{3}{4}$ is the same as **0.75**.

Math Words and Ideas, p. 70

Math Words and Ideas

Adding Decimals (page 2 of 2)

Nadeem and Amelia get exercise everyday by going for a walk together. They keep track of their walking in a log in which they record how far they walk each day. Here is the beginning of one of their walking logs.

Day	How Far Did We Walk?
Monday	2.5 miles
Tuesday	2 miles
Wednesday	1.2 miles

How far have they walked so far this week?

Nadeem's solution

I added the whole miles first:
 2 (from 2.5), 2, and 1 (from 1.2). $2 + 2 + 1 = 5$

Next I added the tenths:
 Five tenths plus two tenths equals seven tenths. $0.5 + 0.2 = 0.7$

Then I combined 5 miles and 0.7 miles.

$$\begin{array}{r} 5 \\ + \ 0.7 \\ \hline \mathbf{5.7 \ miles} \end{array}$$

Amelia's solution

I thought about fractions to solve the problem.

$2.5 = 2\frac{5}{10}$

$1.2 = 1\frac{2}{10}$

$2\frac{5}{10} + 1\frac{2}{10} = 3\frac{7}{10}$

$3 + 2 = 5$

$5 + \frac{7}{10} = \mathbf{5\frac{7}{10}}$

2.5 miles

2 miles

1.2 miles

seventy-one **71** SMH

◀ Math Words and Ideas, p. 71

Games

Capture Fractions

You need

- deck of Fraction Cards

$\frac{2}{3}$ $1\frac{3}{4}$

Play with a partner or a small group.

1. Divide the deck into equal-sized piles, one for each player. Players place their cards facedown.

2. In each round, each player turns over the top card in his or her pile. The player with the largest fraction wins, takes the other players' cards, and puts them on the bottom of his or her own pile.

3. If two of the cards show equivalent fractions, those two players turn over another card. Whoever has the larger fraction wins all the other players' cards.

4. The person with the most cards wins. The game can be stopped at any time.

G1 SMH

◀ Games, G1

Games

Decimal Compare

You need

- deck of Decimal Cards (2 decks can be combined if 3–4 people play.)

0.3 three tenths   0.45 forty five hundredths   0.5 five tenths   0.65 sixty five hundredths

Play with 2 or more players.

1. Divide the deck into equal piles, one for each player. Players place their cards facedown.

2. In each round, each player turns over the top card in his or her pile. The player with the largest number wins, takes the other players' cards, and puts them on the bottom of his or her own pile.

3. If two of the cards show the same number (when 2 decks are combined), those two players turn over another card. Whoever has the larger number wins all the other players' cards.

4. The person with the most cards wins. The game can be stopped at any time.

G4 SMH

◀ Games, G4

Games

Fill Two

You need

- deck of Decimal Cards
- 10 × 10 squares, 1 sheet per player
- Crayons or markers (two or more colors) for each player

0.75 seventy five hundredths   0.1 one tenth   0.9 nine tenths

10 × 10 Squares

Play with a partner.

1. Mix the cards and place the deck facedown. Turn over the top four cards and place them faceup in a row.

2. Player 1 chooses one of the faceup cards, colors in that amount on one of the squares on the 10 × 10 squares sheet, and writes the decimal number below the square. The goal is to shade in two of the squares as completely as possible. A player may never color in an amount that would more than fill a square, and may not split an amount to color in parts of two squares.

3. After one of the four cards has been picked, replace it with the top card from the deck. Player 2 then chooses one of the faceup cards and goes through the same steps.

4. Change colors for each turn so that players can see the different decimal numbers. As the players write the numbers below each square, they use plus (+) signs between the decimals, making an equation that will show the total colored in on each square.

5. If all cards showing are greater than the spaces left on a player's square, the player loses his or her turn until a card that he or she can use is turned up.

6. The game is over when neither player can play a card. Players add all of the numbers they have colored in on each square, and combine those sums to get a final total for both squares. The winner is the player whose final sum is closest to 2.

G7 SMH

◀ Games, G7

IN THIS UNIT

A

Addition
 of decimal fractions, 12, 117–119, 121–122, 125–126, 128, 133
 of decimal numbers, 125–126, 130–131
 of fractions, 12, 53–56, 59–60, 61
Assessment
 activities, 50–51, 95, 136, 143–148, 153–156, 159–163
 benchmarks, 15, 50, 95, 136, 143–148, 153–156, 159–163
 End-of-Unit Assessment, 15, 135–137, 159–163
 ongoing. *See* Ongoing Assessment: Observing Students at Work.
 portfolio opportunities, 14
 Teacher Notes, 143–148, 153–156, 159–163
 writing opportunities, 14
Assessment in This Unit, 14–15

B

Benchmarks, 15, 50, 95, 136, 143–148, 153–156, 159–163

C

Comparing
 decimal fractions, 112–113, 114–115, 128, 133
 fractions, 11, 76–77, 79–82, 93, 95, 151–152
 fractions to decimals, 11, 169
 landmarks to fractions, 84–87, 89–91

D

Decimals
 addition of, 12, 117–119, 121–122, 125–126, 128, 130–131, 133
 comparing, 11, 12, 112–113, 114–115, 128, 133
 comparing to fractions, 11, 105–110, 169
 equivalent decimals, 108
 equivalent fractions, 117
 everyday uses for, 105–107
 hundredths, 108–110, 157–158

 notation for, 108
 representations of, 12, 107–110
 tenths, 107–108, 157–158
 thousandths, 108
Denominator, 10, 70–71, 76–77, 79–80, 96–97, 149–150, 167–168
Dialogue Boxes, 164–169
 Are These Equal?, 169
 Comparing Fractions to Landmarks, 165–166
 Conjectures About Fractions, 167–168
 Finding Combinations That Equal 1, 164
Differentiation in This Unit, 18
Differentiation: Supporting the Range of Learners, 18
 English Language Learners (ELL), 18, 28, 36, 43, 53, 95, 106, 113
 Extension, 18, 31, 34, 45, 50, 56, 57, 82, 93, 113, 119, 124, 130
 Intervention, 18, 28, 31, 34, 45, 46, 50, 56, 73, 76, 81–82, 86–87, 93, 110, 113, 115, 119, 124, 130, 136
Distances, 121–126

E

Eighths, 28–31, 59–60
End-of-Unit Assessment, 15, 135–137, 159–163
English Language Learners (ELL), 18, 28, 36, 43, 53, 95, 106, 113
Estimation
 of sums of decimal fractions, 125–126
Extension, 18, 31, 34, 45, 50, 56, 57, 82, 93, 113, 119, 124, 130

F

Family Letters, 31, 46
Fourths
 of different wholes, 42–44
 of a group, 38–39
 of a rectangle, 25–31
Fractions
 addition of, 12, 53–56, 59–60, 61
 of area of rectangles, 10
 combinations greater than one, 54, 149–150

 combinations that equal one, 48–50, 56, 61, 164
 compared to decimal fractions, 11, 105–110, 169
 compared to landmarks, 11, 79–80, 84–87, 89–91, 96, 151–152, 165–166
 comparing, 76–77, 79–82, 84–85, 151–152, 167–168
 conjectures about, 84, 167–168
 of different wholes, 11, 42–45
 eighths, 28–31, 59–60
 equivalent decimal fractions, 117
 equivalent fractions, 11, 12, 27, 34–36, 76–77, 79–82, 93, 141–142, 151
 everyday uses for, 105–107
 fourths, 25–31, 38–39, 42–45, 48–50, 59–60
 greater than one, 10, 69–71, 149–150
 of a group of things, 10, 38–39
 halves, 25, 27, 42–45, 48–50, 59–60, 152
 on number line, 11, 90–91, 95, 96–97
 numerator and denominator of, 70–71, 76–77, 79–80, 96–97, 149–150, 151, 167–168
 ordering, 11, 79–80, 89–91, 96–97
 of rectangles, 25–31, 33–36, 42–45, 57, 61
 relationships between, 59–60
 representations of, 12, 39, 141–142
 sixths, 33–36, 43–45, 48–50, 59–60
 story problems, 40, 45, 57
 strategies for comparing
  one numerator and denominator are double those of the other, 80, 96, 151
  with same denominator and different numerator, 89, 96, 151, 167
  same numerator and different denominator, 96, 151, 167–168
  using one or one half as a landmark, 11, 79–80, 84–87, 89–91, 96, 151–152, 165–166
 student understanding of, 139–140
 tenths, 57
 thirds, 33–36, 43–45, 48–50

G

Games
Capture Fractions, 79–82, 93, 96
Decimal Compare, 114–115, 128, 133
Fill Two, 117–119, 128, 133

H

Halves, 25, 27, 42

I

Intervention, 18, 28, 31, 34, 45, 46, 50, 56, 73, 76, 81–82, 86–87, 93, 110, 113, 115, 119, 124, 130, 136
Investigations Curriculum, 6–7

L

Landmark fractions, 11, 84–87, 89–91, 165–166
LogoPaths **software,** 13

M

Mathematical Emphases, 10–13, 15, 19, 63, 99
Mathematics in This Unit, 10–13
Math Focus Points, 10–13, 16, 19, 24, 32, 37, 41, 47, 52, 58, 63, 68, 74, 78, 83, 88, 94, 99, 104, 111, 116, 120, 127, 132, 135
    for Discussion, 34, 42, 59, 69, 76, 79, 89, 96, 105, 117, 125, 130
Math Notes
    0.3 and 0.30, 117
    Adding Decimals in Grade 4, 131
    Adding Fractions, 54
    Assuming the Same Whole in the Assessment, 95
    Comparing Fractions, 79
    Congruence, 27
    Conjectures About Fractions Comparison, 84
    Decimal Notation in Different Countries, 108
    Fractions of a Group, 38
    A Half is a Half is a Half, 42
    Measuring Area in Square Units, 25, 42

Place Value of Decimal Fractions, 113
    Reasoning About the Triangular Fourths, 29
    Working with Fractions, 33
    Writing a Zero in the Ones Place, 107
Math Workshop activities
    Comparing and Combining Decimals, 128–130, 133
    Comparing Fractions, 91–93, 95
    Fractions, 54–57, 60–61
    Same Parts, Different Wholes, 43–46
Mixed numbers, 10, 69–71, 149–150

N

Notation
    for decimal fractions, 108
Numerator, 10, 70–71, 76–77, 79–80, 96–97, 149–150, 167–168

O

Ongoing Assessment: Observing Students at Work, 14, 27, 30, 34, 40, 44–45, 46, 49, 55, 56, 72–73, 75, 81, 85, 86, 92, 110, 113, 115, 119, 124, 129
Overview of This Unit, 8–9

P

Place value. *See also* Decimals.
    of decimal fractions, 113
    hundredths, 157–158
    Practicing Place Value. See Ten-Minute Math.
    tenths, 157–158
Planners
    Investigation Planners, 20–23, 64–67, 100–103
    Today's Plan, 24, 32, 37, 41, 47, 52, 58, 68, 74, 78, 83, 88, 94, 104, 111, 116, 120, 127, 132, 135
Portfolio opportunities, 14
Practice and Review in This Unit, 17
Practicing Place Value. See Ten-Minute Math.
Professional Development. *See* Dialogue Boxes; Teacher Notes.
Program components, 6–7

Q

Quick Survey. See Ten-Minute Math.

R

Rational numbers. *See also* Decimals; Fractions. 10–12
Rectangles
    eighths of, 29–30
    fourths of, 25–29
    fractional parts equal to the whole, 48–50
    fractional parts of different sizes, 43–45, 57, 61
    halves of, 25
    thirds and sixth of, 33–36
Representations
    of addition of fractions, 53
    of decimal addition, 126
    of decimal fractions, 12
    of fractions, 12, 39, 96–97, 141–142
    of fractions more than one, 70
    of mixed numbers, 149–150

S

Sixths, 33–36
Story contexts, 107
Story problems, 40, 45, 57
Student Math Handbook **minis,** 170–176

T

Teacher Notes, 139–163
    Assessment: Comparing Fractions, 153–156
    Assessment: Identifying and Comparing Fractions, 143–148
    End-of-Unit Assessment, 159–163
    Extending Place Value to Tenths and Hundredths, 157–158
    Keeping Track of the Whole, 149–150
    Strategies for Comparing Fractions, 151–152
    Visualizing Fraction Equivalents, 141–142

Why Are Fractions Difficult?: Developing Meaning for Fractions, 139–140

Teaching Notes
Chart: "Combinations of Fractions That Equal 1," 56
Contexts for Decimal Grids, 107
Cutting and Folding, 26
"Fractions That Are Equal" Chart, 36
Identifying Each Group's Fraction Cards, 72
Limited Space, 91
Pairs or Groups?, 84
Same or Different?, 49

Technology Notes
Using the *LogoPaths* Software, 13
Ten-Minute Math, 9, 13, 16
Practicing Place Value, 9, 16, 21, 24, 32, 37, 41, 47, 52, 58, 101, 104, 111, 116, 120, 127, 132, 135
Quick Survey, 9, 16, 65, 68, 74, 78, 83, 88, 94
Ten-Minute Math in This Unit, 16
Tenths, 57
Thirds, 33–36

V

Vocabulary, 36
decimal, 105
denominator, 27
fraction, 25
landmarks, 84
numerator, 27
sixths, 33
thirds, 33

W

Writing opportunities, 14